SWEEPER of the SKIES

SWEEPER
of the SKIES

*A story of the life of
Caroline Herschel,
astronomer*

FRANCES LOWRY HIGGINS

FOLLETT PUBLISHING COMPANY

CHICAGO   NEW YORK

Illustrated by Allen Carr

Library of Congress Catalog Card Number: 67-21170

First Printing

Follett Publishing Company
1010 West Washington Boulevard
Chicago, Illinois 60607

T/L 8390

SWEEPER of the SKIES

Introduction to a Comet

1

CAROLINE HERSCHEL was snuggled in her bed, sleeping fitfully. It seemed that someone was calling, "Lina." It was her brother William's pet name for her. No one else ever called her that. Could he have come home suddenly from England to surprise his family in Hanover? She sprang up quickly, hopping across the cold floor.

Listening eagerly, she failed to hear William's voice among those coming from the room below. She must have dreamed that she had heard him. Papa and the boys were home from the concert. Perhaps their voices had startled and wakened her. That was Papa's voice, deep and kindly. Jacob's voice was sharper, almost surly, Alexander's was young and eager. William's would be more like Papa's.

Hoping desperately that he might be with them, she

called down the stairs, her voice sounding thin and faint. "Did someone call me?"

It was Papa who answered, "No one called you, Daughter. We are sorry that we wakened you. We were talking about tonight's concert."

She ventured slowly, experimentally down the stairs. When she was halfway down, Jacob saw her. "Papa told you nobody called," he said gruffly. "Get back to bed now."

Ignoring him, she descended slowly to the foot of the stairs, watching for a sign of displeasure from Papa. With a little rush, she crossed the floor to his side, slipping her hand into his. "I like to hear you talking about the concert, Papa," she said with a smile. "It makes everyone seem excited and happy, the way it was when William was at home."

"Ah, it was a fine concert, Daughter. We enjoyed it very much indeed," answered Papa with enthusiasm. Isaac Herschel was the bandmaster of the Hanoverian Guards' Band. A performer on the hautbois, or oboe, and a teacher of many instruments, he was training all his sons to be musicians. It was the only inheritance he could give them on his poor salary. He was proud of their talents and progress.

"Someday I shall play as well on the violoncello as Herr Stein, I hope," piped up Alexander in his eager way. He was almost fourteen now, five years older than Caroline. Already he was a promising violinist.

Jacob laughed at his boyish ambition. Papa said in his

10

kindly way, "Someday indeed you may play as well as your older brothers and become a musician in the band. Remember, it is practice that makes the perfect musician, my son."

Jacob had been playing in the Guards' Band as long as Caroline could remember. His instruments were the violin, the oboe, and the organ. It was his ambition to become a composer also. Believing that his first work displayed talent, his father encouraged him in this line. "Let us take courage from the example of the great Mr. Handel," he said in reply to Jacob's hope, "who went from Hanover to England to make a career in music, even as our William has done."

The mention of William's name brought a sparkle to Caroline's blue eyes. He was her favorite brother, though he was nearly twelve years her senior and had been away from his home in Germany almost three years. He had played the oboe and the violin long before he went to England. At the age of fourteen, he had been an oboist in his father's band. Now he had also become an organist, a composer, and a teacher. "May William come home from England soon now, Papa?" asked Caroline eagerly.

"William successfully follows his vocation in England and it is better so," said Papa seriously, then continuing as he noted the frown on Caroline's round face, "but he may come home for a visit someday, soon, I hope. I shall be glad to see him. I thought of him tonight when we saw the comet."

"The comet is brighter tonight than last week," put in Alexander.

11

"What is this comet, Papa?" asked Caroline. She had heard them talking about it since it had appeared in the sky over Hanover soon after Christmas.

"A comet is a kin of the stars, which someday may become a star," explained Papa. "This is a special comet that appears in the sky at intervals of seventy-five years—now, in 1759, seventy-five years ago, and in seventy-five years to come."

"It's only a star with a tail like a kite," explained Alexander.

Caroline could hardly imagine such a strange and curious thing. "I should like to see this comet, Papa," she announced hopefully.

Papa looked at his small daughter, who seemed very small indeed in her long nightgown. "Your eyes are like stars," he said, pinching her cheek. "You shall see the comet, of course. You may live to see it when it returns to our sky seventy-five years hence; I shall not. Run, put on your warm dress, cloak, hood. We shall have a look at this visitor in the heavens."

Caroline ran up the stairs as if on wings, her nightgown ballooning behind her, her blonde braids bobbing. When she returned, breathless, they were still talking about the comet.

"How old will you be, Papa, when the comet comes again?" Alexander was asking.

"Almost as old as Methuselah." Papa laughed. "Add seventy-five to fifty-two, and you'll have the answer."

Caroline listened with wonder as Alexander did the sum in his head. She could never do sums that way. Arithmetic was a perpetual problem for her, the multiplication tables worst of all.

"And I shall be eighty-nine," continued Alexander, "an ancient, but not too old, maybe. I hope I may be a famous violoncellist by then."

"And how old will I be?" asked Caroline after struggling in vain with the sum.

"Count it yourself," retorted Jacob. "You are almost nine now. Surely you can do that much yourself."

"How old will I be when the comet returns, Papa?" she insisted.

"Seventy-five plus nine makes eighty-four. You will be a very old lady. You must continue to grow, my dear. You are small for your age, more like seven than nine. Come, let us be going. Let me tie your hood." Papa tied the bow under her chin that she had been too excited to bother with. "And put on your mittens," he added, "it's cold outside."

She pulled on her warm, knitted mittens. She had to walk fast, almost to run to keep up with Papa as he strode along the dark, narrow street to the Guards' Parade Ground, where they would have the best view of the sky. They went so swiftly that she couldn't talk, but a thought kept hovering on the tip of her tongue, ready to pop out at the first chance. What would she be doing through the long years until the comet came again? Would her life be just the same as now, for ever and ever?

13

Finally Papa stopped still near the center of the deserted Parade Ground. "Here," he said, "we have a splendid view of the heavens; we are able to see the comet well."

Caroline closed her eyes before looking upward. "Oh, it's like the Christmas pictures without the Christ Child, the kings, and the camels! There it is, there!" She let go of Papa's hand to point with her mittened fingers.

"You are cold, Daughter," said Papa, laughing as if it were a game they were playing. "That is Orion's Sword, the Great Nebula. Try again."

She swept her eyes across the deep blue sky that stretched like a tent above the quietly sleeping town of Hanover. "Oh, I see it now! It's like a kite but so very small."

"It only appears small because it is so far away," explained Papa, who seemed to know all the answers. "Even the tail may be thousands, millions of miles long."

"How far away is it, Papa? As far away as England, as far away as William?"

"Ah, much farther, Daughter, perhaps farther away than the sun."

"Will William see it, Papa?"

"Surely, Daughter. William is interested in the stars quite as much as he is in music. He will see it no matter how busy he may be, going to the concerts and the lessons."

"Is he seeing it now, do you think?" She tried to imagine William looking upward at the comet from some dark street in some strange English town where he was living, playing, teaching.

14

"It may well be, Daughter, it may indeed."

That was a happy thought, as was any thought relating to her dearest of brothers. She could never forget how kind he had always been when the rest of the Herschel family had scolded, punished, or ignored her. "William is like you, Papa, not like Jacob, cross and hard to please."

"Yes, William is a good brother, a good son. He would have made a fine scholar if he could have entered the university instead of the band at the age of fourteen. Jacob is impatient because he thinks only of himself. Were he more patient, it might be better for his music."

Caroline gave a little sigh as they turned homeward. "I don't understand very well about the stars, Papa. Why does a star have a sword?"

"Ah, the sword! That belongs to Orion, the Hunter of the Heavens. See how it hangs from his belt, the three stars in a row; then see far above them the two bright stars that are his shoulders, or supposed to be." Papa pointed patiently until she could make out the starry skeleton that he called a constellation.

"What does this Orion hunt, Papa?" she asked, still puzzled.

Papa was silent for a while. "Perhaps for his heart's desire as do we all," he answered, hoping that his words would have meaning for his eager little daughter.

"Does he ever find it?"

"Let us hope so—he has been seeking a long, long time."

"I was wondering," began Caroline as they turned

15

homeward from the Parade Ground.

"What, Daughter?" encouraged Papa.

"I was wondering, Papa, about when the comet comes again. Will I be just a Cinderella all that long time?"

"*Ach, Aschenbrödel,* she was the busy one, I think."

"Yes, just like me, Papa, always sweeping, dusting, polishing, brushing Jacob's uniform, helping Mamma."

"And you do not like to do these things?" It had not occurred to him that his bright-eyed little daughter might dislike the menial tasks in which she was constantly employed. Her life was the same as that of all little German girls of her station; it was the only life that Mamma had known and was striving to teach her daughter.

"Not for seventy-five years, Papa." She shuddered at the dull prospect stretching endlessly before her.

Papa looked intently at his small daughter whose heart seemed to be reaching eagerly for some unknown goal. "Perhaps we should do something about that," he offered. "Would you like to have some music lessons, learn to play on the violin?"

"Oh, yes, please, Papa, like the boys. Would Mamma let me?"

"We shall hope so. There is the small violin on which the little Dietrich is learning so well. You may have lessons on that if you wish."

"You make me very happy, Papa." She gave a little skip.

"Why, Daughter, you are trembling. Are you cold?"

"Oh, no, Papa, just happy." Her thoughts went racing

before them along the dark street. Already she was putting aside the broom and duster, leaving the chores and cinders, taking up the violin, placing it under her chin, playing on it as her brothers did. She could hardly hope to play as well as Jacob or William or Alexander, but she would feel like one of them—no longer apart and useless. The lessons would be a pleasant diversion from school and chores, something to look forward to through the years. They would make her whole life different, brighter. "Thank you for tonight, Papa—the comet, the stars, everything," she said at the foot of the stairs, "but most of all for the lessons."

"Good night, Daughter. Sleep well."

Caroline Herschel snuggled in her bed, cold, happy, hopeful. A dream of stars, William, and herself danced merrily through her sleep to the music of the little violin.

Dearest of Brothers

2

"LINA!" CRIED THE TALL YOUNG MAN who was taking Caroline in his arms for a brotherly hug, just as she remembered him doing long ago before he went to England. This was no dream but was really, truly her dearest of brothers, alive and at home in Hanover.

"William!" she cried joyously. "You have come home at last. It has been a long, long time. You are the same and yet not the same." She studied him quizzically.

"Taller," he suggested, standing stiffly erect as if he were a soldier at attention on the Parade Ground.

"Yes, taller, and something else, William. I don't know quite how to say it."

"Older, of course," he prompted. "I am twenty-six now, you know."

"Yes, older," she agreed, "and something more than that. I think it is that you are distinguished-looking."

"Distinguished-looking, am I? A prime asset for an ambitious musician and conductor. I thank you." He bowed courteously, then laughed, his blue eyes twinkling in the way she remembered. "And you, Lina, are taller, older too, a young lady now."

"I am fourteen," she said soberly, "but not very tall. Papa says that I may never be much taller than now."

"For a little sister you are just the right size," countered William. "I would not have you different."

"But I am different, William." She laughed merrily. "To Mamma and to Jacob I am still the Cinderella of the Herschel family, but actually I have grown quite daring. You may not believe it, but it is true."

"So?" he questioned, joining in her laughter. "This I must hear, Lina. Tell me all about it." He sat down in Papa's armchair by the hearth.

Caroline grabbed the feather duster that she had been using when he arrived, placed it under her chin, and hummed through a familiar violin air.

"The violin, Lina, you now play the violin!" he cried in amazement.

"Only a little really," she replied, "but still it is something, at any rate, to me. Papa has taught me, is still teaching me. He has had to be quite secret about it, choosing the times when Mamma was busy or away at market or at Sister Sophia's. Somehow I have persevered so that I can now play the second violin in overtures with our little Dietrich and Papa's young pupils."

"Very daring indeed, Lina!" agreed William. "I must hear you play."

"It is our little Dietrich you must hear, William. He is the wonder child of music, performing on the violin with skill since he was four years old. For his first solo at the concert, he was so tiny that Papa had to stand him on the table. He is an engaging little one, charming all the ladies."

"Yes, I must hear the baby brother too," agreed William.

"Alexander is the Town Musician now, though he is only nineteen," she continued. "Every day he plays the *Chorale* from the Market Tower and gives a music lesson besides. He plays the violin and the violoncello divinely."

"Papa should be very proud of his family of musicians, all trained by himself."

"Indeed, he is," chimed in Caroline eagerly. "Jacob, as you may know, has played the first violin in the Court Orchestra since he returned from England. He is a composer besides. Papa is proud of you too, William. I wish you were coming home to stay instead of just for a fortnight or so. Papa's health is not so good now. He works too hard, giving lessons to the neighbor children and copying music scores far into the night."

"Swallows must fly, must leave the nest." William spoke slowly, sadly. "That is how it is with families too, Lina, sometimes."

"Yes," she agreed with a sigh, "it is too true. Jacob is

20

only at home to eat, to sleep and to dress; Alexander gets home only once a day. I fear that I shall never leave the nest, though. Papa says that I am too plain and too poor to hope for marriage; neither am I good for anything else but drudgery. Now I must fly to help Mamma with the supper. It will be special for you, William, I suspect."

The next morning Caroline had to be at the Garrison School at seven o'clock for her regular lessons in reading, writing and, alas, arithmetic. There was also religious instruction in preparation for her confirmation. She did not see William before she left the house. At three o'clock, when her lessons at the school were over, she went for other lessons in sewing and knitting. It was a long day, seeming longer because of her impatience to be home with William. It was six in the evening before she was free to hurry home and renew her visit with her brother. She had remembered many things about the past and the present to tell him.

"Ah, there you are and about time it is," said Mamma crossly as Caroline rushed into the kitchen all out of breath.

"I hurried as much as I could, Mamma. Is there to be something special for William tonight?"

"Something special at Sophia's, no doubt. William has gone to spend a few days with his sister and her family."

"A few days!" Caroline's face clouded as she began to set the table.

"Would you not have your brother spend a few days with his sister who is nearer his age than you are, and for whom he was so proud to make a fine wedding when she married Herr Griesbach?"

"Indeed I would, Mamma. It will make William and all of them so happy. But the days go so fast I shall hardly see him at all before he must go back to England. His visit will be like a dream. I wish he could stay at home all the time now that Papa is so unwell."

"Ah, do not we all wish so?" said Mamma, and she sighed. "Your papa should put his foot down, as he should have done years ago. If William did not have such a craze for learning, he might be content to stay at home. There is no longer the reason for him to be away now that the war is over."

"The war, Mamma! Was that why?" began Caroline, thinking that she was to solve the mystery of William's long absence, which she had never been able to understand. All that she could remember about it was her brother leaving in secret at night, disguised in a great overcoat, and Mamma sending his trunk after him to Hamburg.

"Stop, Caroline, we say no more about it," ordered Mamma sharply. "Have you not enough to do without intermeddling in the affairs of others? For a girl, her first Communion is more important than other peoples' business."

"I study the catechism every evening and say it over in bed. Is my dress finished yet, Mamma?"

"Your dress will be ready for you before you are ready for it, no doubt. Now call Papa and the boys to supper."

After the supper table was cleared, the dishes washed and dried, and the kitchen put in order, Caroline sat in a

corner by the hearth listening while Papa gave nine-year-old
Dietrich a lesson on the little violin. She had her knitting
in her hands and was knitting fitfully as she listened to little
Dietrich play his lesson. Would she play it that way, she
wondered. She stared at her knitting with alarm, measuring
it with her eyes and needles. She had become so engrossed
in the music that she thought she might have made a
mistake.

"Are you knitting a stocking for the giant, Daughter?"
asked Papa with a sly wink.

She smiled wryly in answer. "I don't do that anymore,
Papa, not if I am careful." She knew that he was referring
to her first piece of knitting, a stocking for Alexander that
had turned out to be as long as he was tall, a better fit for
a giant than a small boy. That seemed a long time ago now.

"Will you practice a little on the violin after Dietrich
has finished his lesson?" inquired Papa.

"Not tonight, Papa. Mamma may not like it. She thinks
that I should study the catechism more."

"And should you not?"

"Yes, Papa, for my mind wanders to other things now
that William has come home. I wish he would stay longer,
always."

"I wish it were in my power to arrange for him to do
so, Daughter. I am inviting a company of musicians to hear
him and Jacob play their compositions. Something may come
of it, I hope. Perhaps a publisher. Who knows?"

"Oh, I do hope so, Papa. Good night." Caroline folded

and put away her knitting. When she was snuggled in her bed, she kept repeating the questions and answers of the catechism silently. She hoped that she might be allowed to go to the concert and hear her brothers play their compositions. She hoped that Papa's dream would come true and that William would stay at home forever and forever.

A few days later, when William returned from his visit with Sister Sophia and her family, there was a feeling of joy in Caroline's heart like that caused by his arrival. It was good to have him home again, though somehow there seemed to be very little time for visiting together. Most of the time he was busy arranging and practicing for the concert, talking and arguing with Papa and the boys.

"I would like to hear this concert, Papa," she suggested hopefully.

Before Papa could answer one way or another, Mamma spoke out flatly. "Tonight you will try on your confirmation dress to see what more is needed." The verdict was indisputable, final.

On the evening of the concert, she walked into the room in her new black silk confirmation dress. As usual William was the only one who noticed her. "Ah, Lina, how fine you are looking," he said.

She smiled over his compliment, explaining, "I am to be confirmed on Sunday."

"That is good," he answered. "Now you are quite grown up, a young lady, ready for life."

"Yes, I suppose so," she replied thoughtfully. "I shall

no longer be going to the Garrison School." Her eyes brightened. "I remember when you were confirmed, William, in your new *oböisten* uniform, long ago."

"It is a long memory you have for so small a sister," he countered. "I am sorry that I cannot be at your confirmation on Sunday. I leave for England in the forenoon."

"On Sunday, William?" she faltered, her face clouding.

"Yes, I go at eleven o'clock on the Hamburger *Postwagen*."

"I had hoped you might be there, William, in the pew with Mamma and Papa."

"Believe me, I would like to be there, Lina. I would be very proud of you. But it was all arranged before I left England. It cannot be changed now."

Early Sunday morning, at eight o'clock, Caroline said farewell to William before going to the Garrison Church for her confirmation. She was wearing the new black silk dress brightened with some of the artificial flowers from Sister Sophia's wedding bouquet. She managed to force a smile until she turned at the corner to wave for the last time, then some teardrops splashed on her flowers.

All through the confirmation service, she kept her mind on what she should say and do to be a credit to Mamma and Papa. She wanted them to be proud of her. She had almost forgotten her sorrow over William's going when a blast from the postilion's horn sounded above the music of the church organ. The Hamburger *Postwagen* was bearing away her dearest of brothers for nobody knew how long. It did not bear thinking of, yet she could think of nothing else.

During the bright Sunday afternoon, she walked with her school friends and the members of the confirmation class in the meadow beyond the town brook, looking for spring wild flowers. Above the chatter and laughter, she kept hearing the postilion's horn echoing, echoing. She could not bear to think of going home. It would be too lonely there with only Mamma and Papa and little Dietrich.

"Come, Caroline," called her companions. "Are you not going home with us? It's growing chilly, and we are hungry."

"Coming," she answered. There was nothing else she could do or say. With the postilion's horn ringing in her ears and heart, she followed them to her own door.

A New Life

3

CAROLINE HERSCHEL was studying, studying, studying as she went about her daily tasks of cleaning, scouring, sweeping, dusting, polishing. Though she was older now, past twenty, she was still the "Cinderella" of the Herschel family of Hanover. Though she was older, she was still small, very much as she had been the last time William had come home. Though she was older, she was little wiser.

The subject she was pondering was life, her life, and what she should do to become something more than a household drudge. She had no books to which she could turn for the answer. Nobody, it seemed, could help her with the solution of the most baffling question: What will you do now, Caroline Herschel?

Papa had been most helpful with her problems even

after he had been ill for a long, long time. Then he had had a seizure, a stroke, which paralyzed the right side of his body. For many years he had been confined to his bed, yet he had been able to continue the music lessons for the small pupils of the neighborhood. He had died at the age of sixty-one, leaving four sons who were talented musicians, although Dietrich was only a boy of twelve. Sister Sophia's sons were all becoming musicians too, adding to his honor.

As for herself, she had done nothing to boast of. How could she? She was fitted for nothing but to become a housemaid, a Cinderella, in some other family as she had always been in her own. If only Mamma would allow her to study French as William had done, she might hope to become a governess someday, perhaps.

"French!" Mamma had cried angrily. "You shall not study French. For a girl it is enough to learn to cook, bake, sew, clean."

"Then maybe I can go to the dressmaking school, Mamma," she ventured hopefully. That would be something, might lead to something. Anything would be better than her present prospect.

"Ah, the dressmaking is useful to know. We shall see what your brother Jacob has to say about it."

Jacob had been the head of the family since Papa's death. Before that he had been in England for a time with William, making a name for himself by dedicating a set of six sonatas of his composition to Queen Charlotte. The royal family of England was Hanoverian, homefolks, the Hanoverians felt. King George III happened to be the same age as William.

He was the Elector of Hanover as well as the king of England. Papa always spoke proudly of the way the royal family had fostered the musical career of the great George Frederick Handel in an earlier reign.

"Shall we ask Jacob about the dressmaking school tonight, Mamma?" asked Caroline as they prepared the supper.

"We shall see, perhaps," answered Mamma, not very hopefully.

"It is a good supper we have, one that Jacob likes," suggested Caroline.

"Yes, a good supper," agreed Mamma. "Call your brother, Caroline."

Jacob sat at the head of the table in Papa's place, eating hurriedly, saying nothing. He did not have the friendly ways of Papa and William. At times he was cross, hard to please, but not tonight. He made no complaints about the meal or the way it was served. Now is the time to ask him, thought Caroline.

Evidently Mamma shared her feeling. "Jacob, I was thinking that maybe Caroline should study at the dressmaking school this year."

"Dressmaking, is it now?" he grumbled.

"Dressmaking is useful to know," ventured Caroline.

"Useful, yes," agreed Jacob, rising from the table, "but I will not have you making dresses for other folks. Only to learn to make your own and Mamma's clothes may you study."

Though it was a limited victory, it was better than none,

29

reasoned Caroline. To attend Madame Kuster's classes might be a step toward something good; it might even be the answer to her baffling problem. "When shall I start the classes, Mamma?" she asked eagerly.

"Ah, I do not know how I shall afford the price of it," said Mamma. "Your brother is not so generous with his money."

"But Jacob is willing that I study the dressmaking, Mamma. Did he not say so?"

"Only so long as the money does not come from his own pocket does he approve. I will ask if you may attend the classes for a *thaler* a month."

Caroline's hopes fell. Must she, then, be the Cinderella of the class, sitting in a corner, doing only bastings or such, looked down on by the rest of the students?

She began her new adventure with fear and trembling but was most agreeably surprised. Madame Kuster, the mistress, greeted her in the friendliest manner. The twenty-one young ladies of genteel Hanover families, some of them half her age, seemed not to notice that she was older or different from themselves in any way.

In this happy atmosphere, her confidence returned, her dreams for the future brightened. Perhaps she could become an expert seamstress and in some way use her skill in earning her living. Might not Jacob change his mind when he saw how well she did? Might she not learn well enough to teach a class of younger pupils someday?

Before any of her dreams came to pass, William made

other plans for her future. He was now located in the city of Bath, in England, where he was organist, composer, conductor, and teacher of music. He was prospering as Papa had always said he would. Alexander was with him, making a career for himself by playing the violoncello as he had always dreamed of doing. Some of Sister Sophia's sons were in England, musicians at the court of King George III.

When William's letter arrived proposing that Caroline should join him in England, it was as if the earth trembled as it had at the time of the Lisbon earthquake, one of her earliest and most fearful memories. He wrote that she could be useful to him as a singer.

"A singer, is it?" Jacob had laughed loudly, scornfully.

"Yes, Jacob. William says that you are to teach me singing. Alexander has told him that I have a good voice."

"A good voice for the King, is it?" Jacob laughed, refusing to say another word about so ridiculous a plan.

Then I shall have to teach myself, decided Caroline. She tied a gag between her teeth, imitating solo parts from violin concertos as she went about her household chores. She hoped to learn execution if not singing in this way.

When William arrived in Hanover soon after her twenty-second birthday, it was as if an earthquake again had shaken her life, her heart.

"Ah, William," cried Mamma bitterly, "you have taken Alexander and Dietrich away from me. Now you would take Caroline, whom I need to help me. I am not growing younger, as you know."

31

"Alexander does better in England than in Hanover, Mamma," insisted William. "Caroline may do better also."

"Alexander, yes, but I need my daughter at home, William."

"I will pay for a servant to help you in Caroline's place if you will allow her to come with me, Mamma."

"A servant is not the same as a daughter."

"A servant may be even better, Mamma. How can you know until you try? Let Caroline come to me for two years; if she does not succeed as I am sure she will she shall be returned to you. I shall come in August to fetch her."

"You would always have your own way, William, even to your Papa you would never listen."

"Then it is decided, Mamma," said William. "I shall be back in August to fetch Caroline. Study your singing, Lina, keep on training your voice."

What will you do now, Caroline Herschel? It was the baffling question again with the answer seemingly no clearer than before. Without Jacob's help, how could she learn to sing? He still resolutely refused to have anything to do with the ridiculous scheme.

"If William wishes to make a fool of his sister, he will do so. Let the blame be on his head, not mine."

Again she went about her chores with the gag between her teeth, practicing violin parts. She did not know whether she would be able to go to England as William wished, nor whether she really wanted to go. For one thing, she did not speak the English language. She could only understand a few words of it.

She knew that William and Alexander were doing well there. For herself, it might prove a different matter. She was small, only three inches over four feet in height; she was plain and pockmarked. How could she possibly make her voice so beautiful that her defects would be unnoticed? Surely Cinderella had faced no such problem as this. To go or not to go, she debated with herself, as spring changed to summer in the gardens and streets of Hanover.

She had never been far from home, had never been away from her family. William, of course, was her family, her favorite brother. Surely he would be kinder to live with than Jacob. He was like Papa, kind and thoughtful. Having assured herself in this manner, she began knitting stockings for Mamma and Dietrich, enough to last them for the two years she would be away. Then she started some ruffles for her brothers' shirts—for William or for Jacob, she did not know yet. It would depend on whether she stayed at home with the one or went to England with the other.

When William arrived in August, she was still undecided. He soon put an end to her dillydallying. "Mamma, I have arranged an annuity so that you may have a servant to take Caroline's place while she is away. Would you like Caroline to train her before she leaves?"

"*Nein,* I shall train my own servant if it is to be. Am I not able to do that, William?"

"Surely, Mamma. It shall be as you wish."

All this caused Caroline to feel like a slave being sold

and bought. Now William would be her master as well as her brother. He would be kind if she pleased him. What if she could not? What then? She had not learned to sing as he expected, had not had a single lesson from Jacob. Could she, then, make a place for herself in his home? He had an English housekeeper, she knew.

It was too late to protest now. All the plans had been made for her going. She packed what clothes she had. It was no wardrobe for a singer, surely. William would have to provide for that. Jacob might have been right all the time: it might be a wild scheme she was undertaking.

The town of Hanover seemed different, dearer now that she was leaving it forever. Both the narrow streets where she had walked for so many years in joy and sorrow and the homes of her friends and classmates aroused an unsuspected affection. The Garrison School, which she had attended from her early years to the age of fourteen, seemed a place of fond memories. This was also true of the Garrison Church where she and all the family had been christened and all confirmed with the exception of Dietrich, who would be the last when he finished his instructions. These had been delayed by his visit to England.

"I shall take good care of Caroline and Alexander in my home in England, Mamma," promised William. "I leave Jacob and Dietrich to your care."

"Ah, Jacob will do as he pleases as always. I shall see that Dietrich prepares for his confirmation, as he should have done before this had he not been taken away to England."

"Dietrich received no harm in England, Mamma. Soon he will be a fine violinist playing in the band. You will be proud of him."

"We shall see," said Mamma grudgingly. "Alexander will be better with you, no doubt. He was making friends with the wrong ones here, with the wild young men."

Caroline wondered how Mamma knew that. She had always tried to shield Alexander and his youthful escapades from her. Had she not succeeded? He was in William's charge now, for which she was thankful. And she likewise was William's responsibility—for two years, perhaps for life.

By Land and By Sea

4

CAROLINE LOOKED DOWN at Mamma and Dietrich from her seat on the *Postwagen*. They seemed different, smaller and lonely, standing there together. A lump came into her throat when she realized that she might be seeing them for the last time. Suddenly tears stung her eyes, splashed down her cheeks.

"*Auf wiedersehen!*" she cried huskily, waving one hand, grabbing her hat with the other as the *Postwagen* started with a jerk.

William, seated beside her, waved, then settled sedately in his seat. She wiped her eyes, struggling with her flyaway hat and ballooning skirts. Soon Hanover was left behind, appearing through the clouds of dust as a cluster of trees with the tall somber-looking Market Tower and the lanthorn

36

steeples of the churches protruding above them.

They were driving steadily westward between the flat, fertile farmlands which stretched on and on to the far horizon. The grain had been harvested, leaving fields of tawny stubble growing up with an aftermath of weedy greenery. The goldenrod waved its fluffy, ripening plumes along the dusty roadside.

"Is it to Hamburg we go?" asked Caroline when she had her hat and skirts under control.

"To Holland," explained William, "where we shall board the packetboat for England. We shall cross the sea more quickly this way."

"Ah." She had not known that there were other ways to go to England. Travel was exciting, with everything new to see and learn. However, as the *Postwagen* raced onward through the days and nights, stopping only for meals and changes of horses, it grew monotonous, with one day like another and the nights likewise.

The mid-August sun burned Caroline's nose, cheeks, forehead, eyes. She soon grew to welcome the evenings with their prolonged twilights. Often she fell asleep as they drove through the quiet, dreaming countryside. Whenever she wakened, she would find William sitting erect beside her, studying the stars.

She had forgotten that there were so many stars in the sky and that they were so bright. She had paid little attention to them since Papa used to point them out by name when she was a small child. "Are the stars so bright in England,

William?" she asked.

"Surely, as you shall see for yourself in a few days now."

"Papa showed me a comet once on a winter night," she remembered, "when I was very small."

"Halley's Comet, I presume," ventured William.

"I do not recall that Papa called it by any name but comet. He showed it to me from the Parade Ground, along with some bright stars. He said you would see it in England. Did you?"

"Surely. It had been long predicted. One would not wish to miss it."

"Who predicted this comet, William?"

"Edmund Halley, the astronomer by whose name it is called."

"I do not understand how it could be predicted."

"Of course not. It requires great knowledge and much study for such things. Shall you not sleep again, Lina?"

"Yes, while it is so cool and pleasant. Shall you not sleep too, William?"

"Soon, perhaps, when I have taken stock of the stars. Seldom do I have an opportunity such as this."

It was difficult to keep count of the time as they drove on and on westward. The farms were more or less alike, and so were the villages and even the few towns they passed. At last they crossed the frontier between Hanover and Holland. "Now we are in Holland," announced William. "We shall be seeing windmills and canals. Look, there is a windmill to the right. Its sails are turning."

"So odd, so pretty, just like the picture in the school

book," exclaimed Caroline, feeling herself a bonafide traveler now that they had left Hanover behind them.

"It is useful as well as picturesque," continued William. "The turning sails move a wheel that grinds the grain into meal and flour. Soon we shall cross a canal."

"This is like a river, a little river," cried Caroline with delight as they drove rapidly across it.

"It is the same except that it is man-made, banked with dikes of earth to keep the water from the land. Holland is a very low country, lower than the sea. It is thus they protect it, their homes, their crops."

"Comes there a boat, William? It looks like a little boat on the little river." She watched eagerly as the canal boat came slowly into view, turning for a last look as the *Postwagen* sped on. "Oh, my hat!" She grabbed but the wind had lifted her hat, carrying it over the fields into the canal. "These winds of Holland are so sudden, so rude," she said, sighing.

"I will buy you a new hat," said William. "Look, we are coming nearer to the coast now. With such winds, there may be a storm at sea. I fear that we shall see no stars tonight."

"If there should be a storm, I should like a bed—dry, soft, and warm."

"Are you tired of travel, then, after only five days, Lina?"

"No, William," she said, lying bravely. "Are we not told, 'Nothing ventured, nothing gained'?" They both laughed.

"That is right. We must learn to be philosophical, Lina."

Nothing seemed to disturb William, not even the storm greeting them at the coast. They climbed into the small open boat with their trunk and were rowed out into the rough waters of the North Sea. When they reached the packetboat, they climbed aboard, breathless. They were sheltered inside while the ship caught the fury of the storm. Before they reached the coast of England, two days later, two of the ship's masts were broken. It seemed a miracle that they arrived at all.

Here they were thrown overboard, as it were, with their trunk into the small boat that rowed them to the beach. From there they followed their fellow-passengers to the small inn where all was dry and orderly—that is, all except Caroline, who felt like a half-drowned kitten with her wet skirts flapping, her soggy shoes squishing.

"Is there a room where my sister may put on dry garments?" William asked the innwife.

"Certainly. Let her go with the maid."

Following the maid as she was directed, Caroline slyly watched the other servants slicing the white bread, thin and neat. She returned in her dry clothes, her hair neatly brushed and braided, feeling a different person from the dripping refugee she had been upon arrival. Seated beside her brother, she had a good breakfast. The English bread seemed wonderful, so white, fine, and thin.

"I suppose you have sailed much farther than we did, William, on other journeys," she said to him.

"I have been to Italy. That is farther."

"To Italy. I do not know much about that."

"It is a country of great musicians and great astronomers. Papa must have told you about some of them."

"Alas, I do not remember. I know very little, as you may soon learn. Did you like Italy?"

"I had an interesting experience. When I had spent all my money, I gave a concert—with the harp and with two horns strapped to my shoulders. In this way I earned my fare back to England."

"You are a marvel, William. I wish I were so ingenious." She watched with admiration as he paid the innkeeper with the strange English money. I shall need to learn about this, she told herself.

Bringing along their trunk, they followed their fellow-passengers to the cart that would take them to the highway where they would board the diligence for London. Hardly were they settled in the cart when the horse began to lunge.

"The horse is new; it is not trained to the shafts," cried a fellow-traveler. "Oh, it is running away!"

The driver could not control it. It leaped ahead, turning quickly so that the cart was overturned. The passengers screamed with fright as they were thrown suddenly against each other, those on the outside being pitched out onto the road. Caroline, William, and another man landed in a dry ditch, frightened but unharmed.

Luckily there were no injuries beyond bruises and indignation. The passengers righted themselves, recovered their possessions, brushed the dust, the dry grass, leaves, and chaff from their clothes. While they were thus busied, a gentle-man on horseback rode alongside and stopped to see if he could be of assistance. He helped the driver to calm the frightened horse and straighten the harness, and guide the cart back onto the highway.

"We had need of a good Samaritan," remarked William as their rescuer rode alongside for a distance to see that all went well.

"Yes, quite like in the Bible story," agreed Caroline, settling herself for the ride that would eventually take them to London.

On the tenth day after they had left Hanover, they came safely to London. It was a huge city to Caroline, the size of many Hanovers. Some of the larger buildings were of stone, the others were of brick. The streets were narrow; above the narrowest ones, the upper stories of the houses almost touched. Near the Thames River was a great structure of high stone walls with stone towers looming above them.

"It could be the castle of a giant," cried Caroline excitedly. "Does King George live there, William?"

"No, though it was the home of the kings in olden times. King George has a palace called Buckingham House in West-end, near Westminster, where he lives in winter. In the summer he moves to his Castle of Windsor in the country, farther up the Thames."

"So many houses!" said Caroline. "To be a king must be wonderful."

"King George is a wise king. Some people deride him

by calling him the 'Farmer George,' because of his interest in agriculture, but he fosters music and science also," said William. "For the afternoon, I have business that will take me to West-end. When I return, we shall see something of the city."

It was late in the day when he returned. In the evening they set out from the small inn where they would spend the night, to see the immensity of London town. Though the shops were closed at that hour, many of the windows were lighted. Whenever they passed an optician's shop, William paused to look at the goods on display with the intensity of a child looking at a coveted toy.

"I know not what such things are for, William," said Caroline, puzzled by his interest.

"Lenses such as these magnify many times. With one large enough, a person may view the stars and learn about the universe and how it is made."

Does he think only of the stars, wondered Caroline, as they passed, without stopping, the windows where the ladies' hats were displayed. She was growing weary when they finally turned back to the inn.

"Good night, Lina. Sleep well," said William.

"I may never waken." She laughed huskily. "It is so long since I have slept in a bed, I have lost count—ten nights, I think."

"I am glad you can laugh about it, Sister. It has been a rough trip for an inexperienced traveler."

The next morning, when Caroline was hurrying down

the stairs to join her brother for another sight-seeing tour of the great city, the landlady happened to notice that she had no hat. "You will want your hat, no doubt," she reminded.

"Oh, my hat!" she exclaimed, laughing. "It blew away when we were crossing Holland. Poof! It was gone before I could grab it. Already it has reached the sea to puzzle the mermaids, perhaps."

"Wait, then, we shall see if my daughter's hat will fit you."

That day they went to see the great cathedral of St. Paul's. Never had Caroline seen a church so vast. It was a dizzying effort to look to the top of the immense, towering dome, and was a journey in itself to walk around the base of the huge building which seemed large enough to seat all the townfolk of Hanover. It truly was a marvel. If it was beautiful, she could not say, having no measure for such things.

"Does the King worship here, William?" she asked.

"Only on special occasions. He has private chapels near his palace and his castle. Within here is the organ on which Mr. Handel sometimes performed. If we had more time, we would see it."

"Ah, Mr. Handel. He also came from Hanover and became a great composer. Papa admired his compositions very much."

"His works are beloved in England too, Lina, in fact everywhere."

44

They walked on and on, stopping only for their meals. Feet and eyes grew tired but they still wanted to see the Bank of England, some other fine buildings, and the sights of the great city that were too numerous and bewildering to remember.

At ten o'clock that evening, when the long summer twilight was ending and the first stars dotted the sky above the towers and domes of London, they boarded the coach that would take them on to the city of Bath, where William lived. Once more the brother took stock of the stars while the sister slept at his side, dozing on into the day so that towns and rivers by the way took on a dreamlike aspect. The next thing of which she was aware was entering a strange house.

"Welcome home, my sister," said William. Turning to the lady who met them in the hall, he said, "This is my sister Caroline from Hanover, who has come to live with us."

Caroline tried to open her eyes to greet the lady whom she knew was William's English housekeeper.

"Ah, she is asleep on her feet," exclaimed Mrs. Bulmer.

"She has had a hard journey. Let us have our tea quickly so that she may go to bed at once."

Caroline muttered something sleepily in German. "She says that she is almost annihilated," translated William.

"The poor dear child!" exclaimed Mrs. Bulmer, hurrying to bring their tea.

Little Lessons for Lina

5

CAROLINE OPENED HER EYES. She was in a bed, in a low-ceilinged room that seemed like an attic. Where am I now? she wondered. Is this the inn near the Tower of London? No, for I recall leaving there and taking the night coach for Bath. This is William's home, my home now. Hurriedly she dressed and started down the stairs.

One flight down was the bedroom floor; below that was the first floor to which she remembered coming with William yesterday—or whenever it was. There she was met by Mrs. Bulmer, who acted as housekeeper for her brother. She lived with her husband and daughter on the ground floor. The Bulmers had been kind to the struggling young musician when he had arrived from Hanover, a stranger in a strange land. When they had met with financial troubles, he had repaid them by taking them into his home and finding employment for Mr. Bulmer.

"If you are looking for your brother, he asked me to tell you that he will return soon. Will you not wait in the drawing room?" Mrs. Bulmer opened a door leading from the front of the hall.

"Thank you," said Caroline, following as seemed to be indicated. She entered the most beautiful room that she had ever seen, furnished in "the newest and most handsome style." While she was lost in admiration, her brother returned.

"Ah, Lina, you have wakened. I, too, slept for twenty-four hours." He seemed refreshed, ready for another twelve-day journey.

"Yes, William, the Sleeping Beauty is awake," she said, attempting gaiety. "I am glad that you are recovered so well, so quickly."

"You must be hungry, quite starved. I shall see if Mrs. Bulmer may serve us while we are talking."

"Are you so busy already, William?" she asked when he had returned. She was curious about the life he lived in his fine English house.

"It is now necessary to prepare for the season in Bath, which opens in October," he explained. "Rehearsals for the orchestra must be arranged at once. Alexander is still in Bristol, where he plays in the orchestra during the summer, so I have everything to do until he returns. The music pupils are also returning. You must have a good meal, Lina. When

47

you are rested, there will be much for you to do."

"I am rested now, William. I should perhaps have a hat, though. I would be a greater credit to you if I had a hat."

"A hat you shall have, my pet." He laughed. "It shall be arranged for Mrs. Bulmer or her daughter to go with you to the hat shop."

"I fear Mrs. Bulmer does not understand me too well. I speak the English like a parrot, 'yes' and 'no' and little else."

"Ah, the lessons, too, will be arranged." He made some hurried notes on a pad beside his plate. "Every morning at breakfast we shall practice English together. Soon you will be speaking like an Englander."

"I hope so," she sighed. "I do want to be a credit to you, William."

"That you shall be, Lina, or back you shall go to Hanover, to Jacob."

"Ah!" She must avoid that by all means. The thought of it made her limp.

"When you are rested, Lina, I shall hear you sing," he continued.

Her heart froze. What should she say to that? What could she say but the truth? "I have had no singing lessons, William."

"How is that? Did I not instruct Jacob to train you properly?"

"Jacob only scoffed at the idea, saying he would have

nothing to do with it. All that I know about singing I have taught myself."

"Very well, I shall teach you. Alexander says that you have a good voice. Each day you shall have a lesson, maybe two. The obstinate Jacob shall be shown who is who and what is what."

The next morning William sat at the breakfast table, making notes for his "Little Lessons for Lina" on the pad beside his plate. As they ate, they had an English lesson, practicing the tongue-twisting pronunciations. Then they drifted into their memories of the wonderful stars they had seen from the *Postwagen* on their way from Hanover. This reminded Caroline of her lost hat.

"Do we not forget my hat, William?" she ventured.

"A hat you shall have this very day. Mrs. Bulmer will go with you to the shops."

"I know not how I shall repay you, William," she said gratefully.

"That you may know sooner than you expect. There are many music scores to be copied for the concerts."

"For that I am glad. I have watched Papa copying far into the night for many years."

"Good! Alexander will help you get started when he returns from Bristol. Now I must fly, Lina. Be sure you choose a hat to do me credit." His eyes were twinkling.

"You are the best of brothers, William. I am glad that you have brought me to share your wonderful life."

Is it to some heaven I have come? she wondered,

49

admiring the stately Georgian residences and buildings of Cotswold stone that lined the way to the hat shop. New King Street, where William's medium-sized house was located, led into the stylish Norfolk Crescent, which was lined with truly magnificent houses.

"These houses are all so clean, so bright, as if the sun were shining within them as well as without," she remarked in appraisal of the structures of honey-colored stone.

"Bath is a fine city," agreed Mrs. Bulmer.

"It is finer than London, though not so large. It is most elegant."

Finding a small hat in the shops that were preparing for the season's trade was a problem. It must be small, she insisted, close-fitting so that it would not blow away as her last one had. The large, absurdly shaped ones, like ships, towers, and other oddities that were said to be the mode in London and Paris, would not do for her at all. "I know not how they may be worn in a coach, a chaise, or a sedan chair," she commented as the search continued. Finally she found one smaller, though not small. It was not exactly to her liking, but it was neater and more sensible.

They returned through a bewildering maze of Squares, Crescents, Circles, and Parades to the haven of William's house at No. 7 New King Street. Bath was enchanting, Caroline decided. She did not wonder that fashionable folk from all over England came to seek healing from the mineral springs and to enjoy the fine musical entertainment provided for them.

Breakfast was the best time at William's house, she discovered, though she would have preferred a more leisurely hour than seven. It was at this time that her brother was free from the tasks that kept him on the run through the day. He was more friendly, like the charming companion she had known and loved from childhood. The daily lessons in English went along merrily, inevitably drifting into their memories of the stars over Hanover and Holland.

"Are there not stars over Bath, William?" she ventured one morning.

"That is a question I keep asking myself," he replied soberly. "During intermission time at the concerts, I step outside just to know that they are there. To study them, there is no time at all."

She was beginning to understand why he had no time for that which he loved best of all. His days and nights were crowded with activity. On Sundays he played the organ, the finest pipe organ in all England, in the new Octagon Chapel, and he directed the Chapel Choir for the morning and the evening services. Previously he had arranged and conducted the rehearsals for them. Sometimes he composed an anthem, a chant, or a psalm for the choir, which required extra rehearsals.

Caroline, with the help of Alexander, who had returned from Bristol for the opening of the season in Bath, learned to copy the music scores and lyrics. Good old Alexander! They had been pals in Hanover, and she had tried to conceal his pranks from Mamma. Now their comradeship was resumed. He played the violoncello divinely, gave lessons on various instruments, arranged the rehearsals for William's great orchestra of nearly one hundred members, yet found time to join her in walks about the enchanting city.

"I did not know there was such a wonder," she exclaimed as they were exploring the new Pulteney Bridge, designed by Robert Adam, the architect. "Why is it called a bridge? Is it not rather a street with shops and houses as the others?"

"Quite so, but wait until you have seen the outside also."

They strolled past the fashionable shops with their costly goods designed for the fine folk who came to take the waters of the famous mineral springs which dated back to Roman times. They paused on the embankment to see the handsome exterior of the bridge.

"Now I can believe it is a bridge," agreed Caroline, "now that I have seen the river flowing beneath it, placidly as in a dream, and the willows leaning toward the water. Oh, the swans, the beautiful swans! What is the name of this river, Alexander?"

"This is the Avon River, which flows into the Channel at Bristol; it has no connection with William Shakespeare's river of the same name."

"Is this Bristol, where you play in summer, Alexander?"

"Yes, in the Theatre Royal, an elegant building. Someday you shall see it, even sing there, I suspect."

"Does William perform there too?"

"He conducts Mr. Handel's great oratorios there in the

Lenten season."

Caroline found everything thrilling about the life of her brothers, which she was being groomed to share. Lessons, lessons, lessons filled her days. At breakfast were the lessons in English, pleasant interludes with her brothers, whom she saw but briefly during the rest of the day. After breakfast came the lessons in English cooking in the kitchen with Mrs. Bulmer. A great waste those, she thought. What good they could possibly be but to practice English pronunciation she could not fathom. Who would want to eat such strange dishes?

Soon William added account-keeping to her "Little Lessons." Each Sunday he gave her a purse of English money for the household expenditures which he taught her how to enter in a small book. This was a fearful undertaking for one whose multiplication tables were in her pocket instead of her head. As she mastered the simple accounts routine, William added lessons in algebra, geometry, and trigonometry, thinking she might find them as relaxing as he did. How wrong he was!

Soon she was promoted to marketing, a still more fearful undertaking. "I shall have to ask your patience, William," she said, recounting the experience of her first day at market when fishwives, butchers, and greengrocers began shouting their wares the moment they saw her coming. "I snatched whatever was first just to get away from the terrible din and confusion. What they were saying, I know not."

"You will learn in due time, Lina, I am sure. Already

you make it seem amusing."

"It was far from that, I assure you, William. I do not understand their English nor they mine. I should have a vocabulary of blocks in a bag like the people in *Gulliver's Travels*."

William smiled as he made some notes in his "Little Lessons for Lina." Alexander, having learned English ways more recently, found it far from amusing. On market days he followed his sister's steps at a distance, ready to reveal his presence if needed. How she would have laughed at his doleful face and sleuth-like manner if she had caught sight of him—which he made sure she did not.

Caroline's daily singing lessons were crowded between the other lessons for voice, oboe, violin, harpsichord, and guitar which William gave in his handsome drawing room. Soon he arranged for her to have dancing lessons at Miss Fleming's fashionable school.

"A singer must know how to make her entrances, her bows, her exits, how to control her hands and arms. You need not tell the good Miss Fleming, but keep these things in your mind, Lina."

"Have no fear, William," she said. "I shall do you credit. I shall not come trudging onto the stage like a peasant or bow like a country cousin."

He laughed. "You have a ready wit, Lina, as well as natural grace."

Alexander laughed with him, as he seldom did. She is good for him, decided William. He is far too serious for a young man of twenty-seven, a "Dick Doleful," as Lina calls him. I trust he has not been homesick in our bachelors' hall.

The Bath season careened dizzily by. With the approach of Lent, preparations were begun for the annual performance of Handel's oratorio, *The Messiah*, which Handel had composed for Easter instead of Christmas, as it came to be given in afteryears. Alexander helped his sister check through the scores for the great orchestra of nearly one hundred members, and the lyrics for chorus and soloists.

"This part for the treble soloist is divine," reflected Caroline, half to herself, as she set about copying it.

"It is your part," spoke up Alexander to her surprise. "Someday you will sing it."

"Now you are teasing me, Alexander, as you did when a boy. I cannot believe you." She rested her pen to consider the prospect.

"Indeed not. You shall see that I am no false prophet. Are you not even now singing in the Chapel Choir? The time will surely come when William will assign this part to you."

"To me?" She was trembling. "The choir was not at all frightening after a few rehearsals, but to sing with William conducting his great orchestra is a dream that takes my breath away."

Soon after Easter, as was the custom, the season at Bath ended. William composed an anthem for the Octagon Chapel Choir to perform on Whitsunday, bringing a final

55

flurry of copying and rehearsing. Then the visitors to England's most fashionable spa went their separate ways, many of the music pupils among them. The theater was closed, the great orchestra disbanded. The city seemed deserted, and the home of the Herschels on New King Street was strangely quiet.

Summer Schedule

6

NOW OUR LIVES will be quite different, thought Caroline. With the season over, I shall see my brother William more frequently, I hope. During these last busy weeks, he has become almost a stranger to me. I can close my eyes and see him conducting Handel's oratorios—so tall, handsome, dignified, with such an air—else I should hardly recall how he looks.

If she expected the lives of the Herschels to settle into some normal, leisurely routine, she could not have been more mistaken. No sooner was William free from the responsibilities of the Theatre, the Pump-Room, and the Chapel than he was asking for his books on astronomy, fluxions, harmonics, and optics, abandoned through the busy season.

"Your books are on the shelf where you left them,

William, where they were when I arrived. No one has touched them except to dust them." She took them from the shelf, handing them to him one by one.

"Ah, Ferguson!" he exclaimed as she added the last one to the pile in his arms.

"Was he, then, so great, so wonderful?" she asked with curiosity.

"A self-taught astronomer, a mere shepherd lad who began the study of the stars alone, unaided, in the fields at night. When he had made a name for himself in Scotland and England, King George made him an allowance for continuing his studies and writing his book, which is most helpful with the theories of Newton."

"Newton, the astronomer of whom Papa used to speak, I presume."

"Astronomer, discoverer, inventor, scholar of the highest rank to whom the world of science is eternally indebted."

"Newton," repeated Caroline, not suspecting that the name would soon be as familiar to her tongue and ears as that of the great George Frederick Handel.

"Sir Isaac Newton," added William reverently as he turned to leave the drawing room, his arms piled with the precious books.

"But, William, shall you not wait for supper?" she cried in alarm. "I shall see if the servant may bring it earlier."

"No Lina, tonight I shall have some milk in my room as I read and rest. I am tired."

"That I do not doubt, Brother, after your busy, busy

season. I shall bring the milk for you." With a jug of milk
and a bowl, she followed him up the stairs to his bedroom,
helped him to settle comfortably with his books, listened
as he read some lines that to him were enchantment, to her
pure puzzlement.

"I think I may sleep for twenty-four hours, Lina." He
smiled wryly.

"As we both did after our journey from Hanover," she
replied. "I hope you do so, William. It would be good for
you."

Later in the evening she tiptoed into his room to find
him asleep over the books as a child over its toys. She could
not remember him when he was small, for he was nearly
twelve years her senior. Strangely now she felt the older of
the two. "Sleep well. May you dream of Sir Isaac, Sir
William," she whispered, closing the door softly. "I wonder
what made me say that?"

The few music pupils who lived in the city continued
their lessons in the summer as did Caroline. Between her
lessons, she went regularly to the market, watching the
spring change into summer in the quiet city. What a pity,
she told herself, that the winter visitors should not see it as it
is now. It is a picture with the light-colored buildings
shining through the greenery, the swans loitering on the
river, the willows trailing their branches in the water.

"I wish I might take some of this beauty into the house
with me," she said as she returned to No. 7 New King
Street. Entering the house, she noted a strange sound coming

59

from the drawing room. She put her ear to the door to try to determine what it was but could make nothing of it. As she stooped to the keyhole, Alexander came in.

"Your posture is neither graceful nor elegant," he chided. "Miss Fleming would hardly approve of it."

"Sh-sh! What is the instrument in the drawing room? I cannot make it out."

"The instrument is a cabinetmaker's saw, Miss Polly Pry."

"Makes William, then, a change in his handsome drawing room?"

"William makes changes in the entire house. If you do not believe it, come to my quarters." She followed him to the bedroom where he had been setting up the turning-lathe that he had brought from Bristol to grind glasses and eyepieces as well as to turn wooden patterns. "When you next visit me, you may hear a composition stranger than Handel's *Fireworks Music.*"

"Ah!" said Caroline. "The servants will never stay with all this noise and confusion. They are difficult even now."

"Servants may be the least of our problems," bantered Alexander. "Wait till William begins the construction of his telescope."

"Telescope!" she echoed. "Makes William, then, a telescope?"

"What else?"

"But I thought that he had borrowed or rented one already."

"Which was his undoing," agreed Alexander. "Now he takes it apart to make a bigger and better one. At the age of thirty-five, he hopes to make up for all the years he wasted before beginning the study of the stars."

"I fear that Frederick William Herschel forgets his position."

"He is in love," stated Alexander.

Caroline frowned, perhaps unconsciously. "With Urania, the Muse of Astronomy," Alexander continued.

"Ah, what is to become of us?" She cried in despair. Entering the room where William was patiently polishing a reflector for his telescope, she gasped in horror. The lace frills on his cuffs were trailing in the molten pitch, taking on a smudge that no laundress would ever be able to remove. "Is it now the mode to wear colored frills, William?" she asked, trying not to smile at his intensity.

"I had not noticed." He tucked up the frill now that it was too late.

"Will you join us for supper now, William? We have some of the home dishes that you like so much."

"No, Lina. I cannot stop until the polishing is finished. Science is a master that demands patience and perfection."

"Would this science object if Alexander or I took your place while you eat? You must eat, William."

"I have told you it is not possible to stop until the polishing is completed. It may take many hours yet."

"And you have been polishing for many hours already! I shall bring your supper and feed you as I would a child."

She brought his supper, patiently feeding the intent polisher who seemed tireless at his messy, monotonous task. After she removed the plate, she returned with a book to settle in a chair beside him. "I could not find your favorite, *Dean Swift,* so I have brought *The Arabian Nights.* I know you like that also, William."

She began to read aloud to him as she used to read to Papa while he copied music scores far into the night. Little did she reckon that here was beginning a companionship that would be extended beyond "one-thousand-and-one-nights" to a whole half-century. Soon she was drawn into the scientific activity of the household, joining her brothers in making bigger and better telescopes.

Her first task was to patiently fashion tubes of pasteboard into which would fit the lenses ordered from the opticians of London. Bath still had no opticians' shops such as had lured William's eyes and feet as they tramped the London streets the previous summer. The pasteboard tubes proved unsuccessful, being too long and too limp to support the weight of the lenses. Someone had to hold them in line while William attempted hurried glimpses of the stars. They were discarded in favor of tubes of tin or copper.

"Would it not be an economy to buy a telescope, William?" ventured Caroline, aghast at all the wasted activity and material.

"If you but knew the price that is asked for the smallest Newtonian telescope, Lina, you would not need to ask."

"Is it a Newtonian telescope we are making, William?"

"We are making both Newtonian and Gregorian telescopes of the smallest size. When we have perfected our skill, we shall attempt a five-and-one-half-foot Gregorian with which we may hope to review the heavens as they do at the observatories."

When he was not polishing a metal reflector for one of the experimental telescopes, William regularly joined his brother and sister for meals. On the pad which he kept beside his plate he no longer jotted down the "Little Lessons for Lina" but instead sketched designs for improving the stands for the telescopes which the cabinetmaker would construct in the drawing room.

As the so-called summer vacation passed, William sometimes surprised his co-workers by composing a glee, a catch, or an anthem to be used in the winter programs. Then Caroline would desert her task of the moment to copy the scores and the lyrics. Alexander, glad for the excuse, would leave his turning to arrange for a rehearsal in the drawing room, where the cabinetmaker's latest product would be pushed aside or used as a music stand.

William Herschel, it was evident, had not lost his cunning at composing or conducting while working at his menial vacation tasks. Alexander's technique on the violoncello was not impaired by the long hours he had spent at the turning-lathe. He played as divinely as ever, decided Caroline. Her voice was steadily improving in spite of the long sessions of reading aloud to William from such favorites as *Don Quixote* or the novels of Laurence Sterne and Henry Fielding. The visitors to Bath for the coming season would be offered their usual fare of fine music to relieve the tedium of what they considered a country town. No need to worry about that yet.

After rehearsals, the musicians would return to their machines, working feverishly to make up for the interruptions. To Caroline, the marketing that she formerly had dreaded became a welcome diversion in the fresh air and sunshine. In these days the hatless, half-drowned country child who had arrived on the coast of England the year before seemed less like herself than some character from a storybook. The one person responsible for her transformation was William; but for him she would still be at home in Hanover, facing Jacob's frowns.

"Alas!" she cried as she considered this. "Am I not as much given to frowns and grumbling as Jacob?" She was overwhelmed with remorse.

It was difficult not to grumble at the disorder that made the house more like a factory than a home. But was it not William's house to do with as he pleased? She would watch her sharp tongue and try not to chide him for putting the stars above the music that was his livelihood, their livelihood. Surely it was his right to become a scientist, inventor, maker of telescopes, polisher of reflectors, minder of the heavens, if he chose. Had not Papa always said that he would have been a fine scholar if he had but had the chance? It must never be said that Caroline Herschel was a hindrance to the career of her favorite brother.

Alexander, overtaking his sister at the corner of New King Street one day, cried, "Lina, you look very doleful. What is the reason for this?"

"Doleful I am," she answered sadly, "for I dreamed that William grew tired of my grumbling and sent me home to Jacob."

"Send away the singer who will someday replace Miss Linley or Miss Farinelli? That William will never do, Lina. Grumpy you may be and a fraud, with your multiplication tables in your pocket instead of your head, but William has polished you as tirelessly as one of his reflectors. Should you displease him, he will but polish the more."

"Ah, I hope so! I have been here a whole year now and it is home to me. I could not bear to leave."

"Miss Caroline Lucretia Herschel," announced Alexander playfully as he opened the door of No. 7 New King Street.

Caroline entered with a curtsy. Smothering her laughter, she said, "If you will kindly order the tea, my good man, I shall tell my brother that it comes at once."

Bath Theatre Debut

7

AS AUTUMN DESCENDED on the county of Somerset, the spa of Bath began to waken from its summer sleep. Burnished leaves appeared on beeches, elms, and oaks, wafting earthward to reveal the stately Georgian buildings of honey-colored Cotswold stone. Gold-splashed willow leaves fell into the placid Avon to drift silently downstream among the swans. Flocks of migrant songbirds paused in the gardens for final symphonies.

In their wake would come the human migrants who, on doctors' orders, would seek healing from the mineral springs where the Romans had bathed a thousand years before, leaving magnificent ruins recently discovered beneath the eighteenth-century establishment. To England's fashionable spa would come all the types portrayed in the letters of

Walpole, the dramas of Sheridan, the novels of Fielding, Sterne, and Smollet.

Soon would arrive by coach and chaise, lords and ladies of high degree, politicians, judges, clergy, literati, wits, beaus, beauties, fortune hunters, adventurers, gamesters, rogues. Inns and lodging houses were preparing to receive, shelter, and feed them. Shops were making ready to tempt them with fashionable goods.

Mr. William Herschel, the handsome conductor of the Theatre orchestra, was preparing for another brilliant season of musical entertainment. He was reassembling his great orchestra of nearly one hundred members, conducting rehearsals, and composing selections for special voices and occasions. In the midst of all this, he was welcoming the pupils who were returning for lessons in voice, on the oboe, violin, harpsichord, and guitar.

This season he would not need to be on the alert for a new and pleasing voice, nor would he require Miss Farinelli, the Italian singer, as he had previously. He now had a singer trained by himself through the years as a substitute, he hoped, for the celebrated Miss Linley, the pride and pet of Bath before her marriage to the playwright Sheridan and her removal to London where she was continuing her fabulous career.

He had trained his sister Caroline with the Octagon Chapel Choir and at little parties in his drawing room, where she had sung the popular glees and catches. Pleased with her progress, he had included her in the choruses for Handel's

67

oratorios—*The Messiah, Samson, Judas Maccabeus,* and others. Then, quite confidently, he had assigned her to assist in training the choruses. He now considered her ready for her debut in the part of the first treble, as the soprano was called then, in *The Messiah.* She was small, childish in appearance, somewhat shy, yet her voice was sweet and true. He was satisfied that she could please his audiences at the Theatre.

"Lina," he said one morning at breakfast, "you will require a new gown for the concerts." He handed her some bank notes.

"Ten guineas," she said excitedly. "I shall be as fine as the Queen."

"It should be suitable and becoming," he cautioned.

"Have no fear, William. I shall dazzle so that your fine ladies and beaus shall not hear my voice for the splendor of my gown."

"Alas, fine feathers do not make fine birds! Come, Lina, let us practice before the pupils arrive for their lessons."

"Good luck!" Alexander called after them as teacher and pupil disappeared into the drawing room.

"Remember," warned Caroline over her shoulder, "you shall escort me to the best, the most fashionable dressmaker in the city."

"In a sedan chair, I presume."

"Indeed. How else arrives a singer, the sensation of the season?"

"Begin," said William, impatiently touching the keys of

the harpsichord.

"We do but have our little fun, William," sang Caroline in falsetto.

He raised his hands to his ears in horror. "Now, Lina," he commanded sternly, poising his fingers once more on the keys. "Let it not be said that Jacob Herschel is a prophet."

She had learned that it was not difficult to sing for William. He seemed to wield a magic wand that transformed her into a singer with but slight effort on her part. Her confidence, as his, had grown with the seasons. She had no fear of attempting the part of treble soloist in *The Messiah*.

Shy, sweet, proud in her fine new gown, she made her debut in the Bath Theatre, singing naturally and confidently, finding it no more frightening than a pleasant dream. Mr. Palmer, the manager of the Theatre, assured her that she was "an ornament to the stage." Fine ladies complimented her pronunciation of English.

Though she was not called "Siren" or "Angel" as was the celebrated Miss Linley, or painted by George Romney and Sir Joshua Reynolds as that beauty had been, William was pleased with his prima. Soon she was singing with him five nights a week at Bath or at Bristol, a ten-mile drive down the valley of the Avon River. To her surprise, the news of her success spread beyond Somersetshire and Gloucestershire, beyond the neighboring spa of Cheltenham, to the Midlands. The city of Birmingham invited her to sing at its music meeting, as the music festival was then called.

"Congratulations!" cried Alexander excitedly when she

told him how the invitation had been extended in person at the close of her performance in *The Messiah* at the Bath Theatre. "Remember," he bantered, "I discovered you. But for me, William would never have heard of your voice—or Birmingham either."

"Will William conduct, I wonder?" she asked seriously.

"It is not William but you who are invited to sing at their music meeting. This is a great honor, Lina, believe me."

"Then I shall not sing," she decided loyally. "I shall sing only where William conducts. He has made me all I am."

"Beware that he does not unmake you," warned Alexander, intending only to banter but touching nearer the truth that he suspected.

"What nonsense is this?" cried Caroline indignantly. "I have toiled faithfully to please William with my voice. Shall I not do as much to please him in any way he may desire?"

"Even though he should take you a farther, more hazardous journey than from Hanover to Bath?"

"How he could do that I know not, for I barely survived. But why are we so doleful all of a sudden? Should we not be gay? Soon the season ends, rehearsals and concerts become things of the past, merely memories."

"I thought you disliked the house turned upside down, with litter and confusion everywhere."

"Alexander, you try my patience," she began when William came in with an anthem he had composed to be

70

performed in the Octagon Chapel on Whitsunday. It would have to be copied at once so that rehearsals could be included in the already overcrowded schedule. She reached for it, grateful to end her silly quarrel with Alexander.

As she fetched the copying materials, she overheard William requesting his brother to take charge of a pupil who was coming for a lesson on the violin. He wanted to finish a drawing for something concerning his telescope. It was true, of course, as Alexander had reminded her, the house would soon be topsy-turvy with the making of telescopes.

William could never bear to be idle. "It kills me to do nothing," he often said. Come season's end, he would rest for a few days or perhaps only twenty-four hours, then plunge the household into disorder in the pursuit of his dream. Alexander, the expert mechanic, would operate the turning-lathe for his brother. Caroline, in addition to her housekeeping responsibilities, would find various ways to be helpful.

Their first satisfactory telescope was a five-and-one-half-foot Gregorian. Completed before the end of the Bath season, it was set up with pride and hopefulness in the garden at No. 7 New King Street. Through it, on a memorable night, William saw "the lucid spot in Orion's sword belt and the rings of Saturn which appeared like two slender arms." This poetical observation, made on March 1, 1774, was the first entry in his astronomical journal, which he would keep faithfully for fifty years.

Thus the self-taught astronomer with his homemade instrument began the career that would startle the observatories, universities, and learned societies. He called his self-assigned task "minding the heavens." He was thirty-six years old but was striving to make up for his wasted years by his industry and intensity. The loyal Caroline, just turned twenty-four, minded the heavens by minding her brother through his vigils from dusk to dawn. This brother-sister team of astronomers was absolutely unique in the history of the planet Earth.

Their next construction project was a seven-foot Newtonian telescope with an aperture of four-and-one-half-inches, magnifying two-hundred-twenty-two times. To Caroline, with her multiplication tables in her pocket, it must have been awesome to contemplate such magnification.

Astronomy was no mere hobby to William, but the means of studying the structure of the universe, of looking farther into its mysteries than any man before him. With the seven-foot Newtonian set up in the Bath garden, he began his first review of the heavens, studying all the stars of first, second, third, and fourth magnitude.

Caroline, seated at a table beside the telescope, noted down his observations. Eyes and hands occupied with the telescope required assisting eyes and hands for making the notations of time, location, and distance of the findings. The sister recorded this invaluable data. Soon she had learned to reduce and revise it for him.

When William paused after a four-hour stretch of observation, as common sense and even his uncommon stamina demanded, she brought the milk or tea for their refreshment break. Then the minding of the heavens was resumed, to be continued until the stars became invisible and the skylarks, likewise invisible, sang above the fields of Somersetshire. Whereupon the two weary astronomers trudged across the dew-drenched garden to breakfast and to bed.

Later in the day, or on stormy nights, the observer would review his notes, making the deductions to be incorporated into scientific reports which would be patiently transcribed by his sister. This was to be the pattern of their lives for a half-century, broken only by unfavorable weather, emergencies, and the Bath season. The season which provided the bread and butter and the very instruments for the celestial activity was an unfortunate interruption, William thought. The lessons, rehearsals, and concerts became more and more irksome to Herschel, who would have preferred to devote all his time to the study of sun, moon, and stars.

"We need a larger house," he announced to his co-workers, as a dream for a larger telescope took shape in his mind.

"What shall we build next, William?" asked Caroline with wonder.

"A ten-foot Newtonian, perhaps a twenty-foot."

"Ah!" She had not suspected that there could be such huge instruments.

Twice they had moved in quest of larger working quarters, better observation sites. Finally they settled at No.

5 Rivers Street, in the upper, more fashionable part of the city, near the Royal Crescent, the Circle, the Assembly-Room, and the home of the Literary and Philosophical Society of Bath. William was pursuing his studies of the moon, counting its mountains, estimating their heights with his seven-foot Newtonian. Often he set up his instrument in the pretty little square in front of the house.

One night, as he was engrossed in his observations, a passing stranger stopped to observe the novelty of an astronomer at work in Bath. He asked permission to look through the telescope, which was readily granted. The next day he returned to thank the astronomer, or so he said, introducing himself as Dr. William Watson, a physician of Bath and a Fellow of the Royal Society. His father was Sir William Watson, a physician of London and a scientist whose discoveries in the field of electricity had won him the coveted Copley Medal of the Royal Society.

From that time on, Dr. Watson became an intimate of the Herschel household, being drawn inevitably into the fascinating scientific experiments. He invited the astronomer, who impressed him as being a superior and intellectual gentleman, to join the Literary and Philosophical Society of Bath. He urged him to prepare some astronomical reports for the Royal Society.

William Herschel excitedly assembled from his faithfully-kept astronomical journal a year of observations of the variable star, *Stella Mira*, "Wonderful Star," in the constellation of *Cetus*, "The Whale." For good measure, he assembled a second paper on his observations of the moon, its mountains, cavities, and volcanoes. These papers were his introduction to the world of science, his first step toward recognition. Discoverer Herschel had been discovered.

Onward to the Stars

8

A SERIOUS INTERRUPTION to astronomical progress in Bath occurred in the summer of 1777, when Mamma wrote that Dietrich had run away from home. It was thought that he and another young Hanoverian had gone to the East Indies.

"Poor Mamma," said Caroline, sighing, "her children are her sorrow."

William, putting aside his turning of an eyepiece of cocuswood, was on his way to Hanover within two hours. He hoped to intercept the runaways in London. There he learned that no ship would be sailing for the Indies before the end of the year. Assuming that Dietrich, with his plans blocked, would go to Bath, he went on to Hanover to comfort Mamma.

Soon after he had left home, a letter came with the

alarming news that the baby brother was ill and alone at an inn near the Tower of London. Since Alexander was in Bristol and would be walking home for the weekend, Caroline walked down the Avon Valley to meet him. Alexander withdrew all his savings from Caroline's keeping and set off at once for London. He found Dietrich and nursed him until he was strong enough to be moved to Bath. Caroline then took charge of the convalescent, keeping him by doctor's orders on a strict diet of "roasted apples and barley-water."

When William returned, he took pity on the gaunt young man, putting an end to the nonsensical diet. William knew that Dietrich must be fed properly to regain his health and vigor. When he was recovered, employment was found for him, an easy task since he had been a near virtuoso on the violin since childhood.

During this stay in Bath, Dietrich became familiar with the astronomical atmosphere so that Caroline could write to him freely of instruments, measurements, and the like. After his return to Hanover, where he married and settled, he had a telescope of his own.

A multitude of studies interrupted by the escapade of the younger brother had to be brought up to date. For six years William had been pursuing his study of the planet Mars, fathoming such mysteries as the action of its polar ice caps, the height of its atmosphere, the length of its year, its distance from the earth. These matters demanded instant attention.

Likewise through the years, the mysteries of the planet Saturn with its atmospheric rings and numerous satellites had attracted him. These, however, eluded him, remaining unsolved. Only with a more powerful telescope could he hope to bring them to a satisfactory conclusion. He began to dream of a thirty-foot Newtonian with a three-foot reflector, making drawings for the truly ambitious project.

A larger and seemingly suitable house for the project was found at No. 19 New King Street. A washhouse in the rear would provide space for a furnace and casting room as well as the other working quarters needed. To the rear of this was a garden and grass plot extending to the river, a perfect site for the nightly observations.

By this time, the Herschel household had learned to move with a minimum of interruption to their astronomical routine. Anxious to lose no time from his sweeping or "rummaging," as he called it, William went ahead to the new home to set up his seven-foot Newtonian. Caroline remained in charge of the cleaning up at Rivers Street. In the quiet riverside garden, near neighbor to the swans of Avon, William kept his nightly appointment with the stars. It was a date with destiny.

The evening of March 13, 1781, while rummaging among the stars of the constellation of *Gemini,* the well-known "Heavenly Twins," his attention was attracted by a star "visibly larger than the rest." He had not observed it previously; it was not listed among the stars of Flamsteed's Star Catalogue. This might mean that it was a comet, though no tail was visible. A curious nebulous star or a comet was all he could make of it.

Twenty-four hours later, with Caroline in attendance, he recorded that it had changed its position. It was definitely a moving body—a comet that was unlike a comet. To determine its true nature was beyond his skill; that was a task for the experts. He promptly reported his mysterious discovery to the Astronomer Royal at Greenwich Observatory, whom he had met at Rivers Street and considered "a devil of a fellow." From Greenwich, the news of the discovery was relayed to all the observatories of Europe.

The discoverer prepared a scientific report for the Royal Society. For want of a more accurate title, he called it *Account of a Comet*. Caroline copied the report as she was to copy volumes of them through the years she was her brother's assistant. As yet, she had not seen the mysterious star. She would see it through a larger telescope after William had made other startling discoveries about it.

Meanwhile the astronomers of Europe had a field day, some agreeing with William's theory that it was a comet, others daring to suspect that it was a planet. After months of controversy and observation, it was definitely determined to be a primary planet of the solar system, moving in majestic orbit beyond Saturn, which had been considered the most distant member of the solar system up until that time.

The discovery of the unknown astronomer of Bath was the sensation of the century, indeed of the ages. Not within recorded history had a primary planet been added to those identified and named in the undated beginnings of time. William Herschel, with his homemade telescope, the seven-foot Newtonian, "had broken the barriers of heaven," as was to be inscribed on his tomb.

"Then felt I like some watcher of the skies when a new planet swims into his ken," the poet Keats was to write in afteryears, undoubtedly referring to the momentous discovery at No. 19 New King Street. Actually the event in the Bath garden the evening of March 13, 1781 had been less dramatic, less fraught with ecstasy than he pictured it. The rummaging was merely routine for William, and he had not known instantly that the star which swam into his ken was a planet. He was, however, proud to be awarded the Copley Medal by the Royal Society and to be unanimously elected a Fellow in that august and learned body. No one was more delighted than Sister Caroline, his faithful assistant.

When a year had passed and the experts had provided no name for his discovery, Herschel proposed *Georgium Sidus,* "Georgian Star," in honor of King George III, who had by that time become his patron. He presented his suggestion by letter to the President of the Royal Society, Sir Joseph Banks. A French astronomer gallantly proposed the name of Herschel as appropriate. Bode, of the Berlin Observatory, proposed the name Uranus, deriving it from Urania, the Muse of Astronomy.

Astronomer Bode's suggestion was approved by his

fellow-astronomers since it was in keeping with the pattern of classical nomenclature set by the anonymous, prehistoric namers of Mars, Mercury, Venus, Jupiter, Saturn. The seventh planet was christened Uranus, and No. 19 New King Street, Bath, became Uranus House.

The Herschels, however, continued to refer to their discovery as the Georgian planet or *G. Sidus*. Meanwhile, no time had been wasted in minding the heavens. The building of bigger and better telescopes had been continued as fast as the usual interruptions would permit. The three-foot reflector for the proposed thirty-foot Newtonian was a tremendous undertaking for amateurs.

It was composed of speculum metal, an alloy of one part tin and two parts copper, a most brittle substance which cracked if cooled too quickly. Since neither of the Herschel brothers knew the first thing about casting, a caster had to be hired for the difficult operation. The family helped in every way possible.

Caroline's task was to convert dried horse dung into loam to be used as the mould for the casting. She sat, patiently pounding it in a mortar with a pestle, then running it through a fine sieve. Alexander, perhaps out of pity, often joined her at the endless, dusty, odorous task. When Dr. Watson came by the house, as was his custom, he also helped with the pounding and sifting, proud to have a finger in the making of the giant three-foot reflector. No observatory then had a mirror of such size and power. No commercial manufacturer had attempted one; only the intrepid William Herschel had dared.

Their first attempt at casting was a near-disaster. The furnace gave way; a half-ton of molten metal ran into the fire and onto the floor of the washhouse, sending the paving stones flying to the ceiling. The caster and his assistants ran for their lives, escaping through the outside door of the washhouse. Exhausted with heat and exertion, William stumbled and fell on a pile of brickbats. The metal was salvaged and reheated; more horse dung was pounded and sifted. The second attempt produced what appeared to be a perfect casting. Examination showed that it had cracked in cooling.

These hazardous experiments in the name of science were ended temporarily by the approach of the Lenten season. One morning during Passion Week, the three Herschel musicians were preparing to go to Bristol for a morning rehearsal and an evening performance of *The Messiah*. The chaise stood waiting at the door. Caroline was filling the music box with the ninety-odd scores to take with them. William was talking to Dr. Watson, who had stopped by to try to persuade Herschel to go to London to meet the members of the Royal Society. At that very moment, the messenger of the gods arrived in the person of George Griesbach, Sister Sophia's oldest son, a member of the Queen's Band. He had come to tell his Uncle William that he was expected at Court with his telescope. It was a Royal Command.

The summons from his king must have touched Herschel

deeply. Excitedly, he began planning with Dr. Watson how to pack and transport his famous telescope to London. Caroline and Alexander welcomed their nephew, who had been driving all night. They took him on to Bristol with them, this being the most they could offer in the way of hospitality. Every evening that week, except Friday, both would be performing in *The Messiah* either in Bristol or Bath.

Despite his excitement over the Royal Command and the coming journey to London, William managed to close the Bath season with his customary dignity and grace, concluding it on Whitsunday at the Octagon Chapel. Caroline, unsuspecting, then sang her swan song, an anthem which William had composed for the occasion. Never again would the brother or sister perform together at Bath or elsewhere. That chapter of their lives was ended.

As soon as he could arrange it, William hastened to join Dr. Watson, who had gone ahead to his father's house near Lincoln's Inn Fields, London. He took with him the seven-foot Newtonian with a stand and steps fitted into a box which was ready to be screwed into position on arrival. Also among his baggage were his first catalogue of double stars, recently published in the Philosophical Transactions of the Royal Society, Flamsteed's Star Catalogue, a micrometer, tables, and sundry equipment.

Caroline watched him drive away, happy he was receiving the recognition he so well deserved. Papa would have been proud, she thought, that he had been able to succeed without the education Papa could not give him. The same age as King George, now in his forty-fourth year, he had come far indeed. A talented and successful musician. An acknowledged astronomer, though wholly self-taught. His life was like a story or a dream.

It became more dreamlike as the days passed without a letter from him. It was as if he had vanished to his own planet. They were concerned about his welfare and curious about his reception at Court. When his pupils began to inquire about their interrupted lessons, they were annoyed that there was no answer. Mr. Palmer, the manager of the Bath Theatre, likewise had to be put off, pending word from William.

After two weeks of mixed emotions, they received his first letter. He was well, for that they were thankful. He was delayed, that was evident. He had been presented to King George and Queen Charlotte. The King had talked to him about astronomy and had expressed a wish to see his planet through his telescope. That would be arranged in due time. The telescope was now set up at the Greenwich Observatory where it was the envy of the Astronomer Royal. He could not leave until the King dismissed him. Mr. Palmer and the pupils must be so informed.

"The King has inquired about you, Alexander," read Caroline excitedly.

"About me and the great speculum, I see," read Alexander over her shoulder. "Whether that is an honor, I doubt very much. I would prefer that he would set a date for

William's return. This dilly dallying may cost me dear. I shall have to stall Mr. Palmer again."

"We should be thankful that William is well and well-received," Caroline exhorted. She had been overly optimistic. A later letter informed them that he had suffered a slight attack of the influenza but was recovered. The King had moved his Court to Windsor Castle for the summer, and he had followed. He was being lionized by the best company, which often was less pleasing than polishing a speculum. He had been granted another interview with the King, who had ordered George Griesbach to play a solo concerto on his oboe for him. He could not leave until he was royally dismissed. He wished money and clothes sent to him.

Soon came a more disconcerting message. " 'Everything looks very like as if I were to remain here,' " read Caroline aloud. "What can he possibly mean by that? Has he not a career here in Bath? The King should not detain him so. I know that he longs to be back at his work, his polishing of speculums, his casting of them. He is now more than a month behind in his studies of the stars. No one minds the heavens when he is away."

Dr. Watson had returned from London after staying a few weeks. Two months passed with more requests for money before William followed him. He brought what he considered the most exciting news. At last the King and his councillors had reached a decision. They had offered him the position of court astronomer with an annual salary to be paid by parliament. He was to live near Windsor

Castle, act as "showman of the heavens" to the King's guests, give lessons in astronomy to the Royal Princesses, and perform other tasks associated with astronomy.

Dr. Watson, feeling himself largely responsible for the upheaval, was shocked. He considered the salary a beggarly sum for a scientist of Herschel's stature and reputation. William, happy to be freed from his duties as a musician, had not quibbled about it. He had obtained permission to manufacture and sell his telescopes that had become the envy and wonder of the world—which would more than compensate financially. Moreover, he was confident that he could conduct his nightly observations with less interruption. No more concerts, rehearsals, lessons! He was as happy as a schoolboy set free from his irksome routine. In an outburst of enthusiasm, he had found and rented a house for them at Datchet near Windsor. He had engaged a maid. They could move at once.

His household was stunned. "Whither thou goest I will go," would have been Caroline's decision whatever the cost. She forced herself to pretend a measure of enthusiasm, which was not easy. She had lived in Bath for ten years, had come to look upon the elegant and beautiful city as her home. She had been too busy to make many friends outside the family, but she had been content, even happy. Moreover, with William's help, she had had a career there. What would happen to that now?

Reluctantly she joined her brothers in packing the household goods and telescopic equipment to be sent ahead to

Datchet in carts. Dr. Watson haunted the house like a ghost. He hoped that he had not pushed his friend into an unwise decision. It had turned out very differently from what he had expected. But it was too late. They were off.

To Caroline, Datchet was a disappointment from the first. The house was a ruin, an old abandoned hunting lodge, shabby and neglected, damp within from the leaking roof, without from the soggy meadows of the nearby Thames River. The garden and grounds were overgrown with weeds. An army of helpers was required to make it habitable.

William had made his choice too hurriedly on the basis of the stables, which seemed to offer suitable working quarters for casting and polishing reflectors, and the laundry, which could be made into a room for storing his growing library of astronomical notes. When the maid he had engaged failed to appear, it was discovered that she was in jail. It was a fortnight before other help could be found. The elderly wife of the gardener showed Caroline the way to the neighborhood shops where goods were poor and prices high.

"We shall live on bacon and eggs," announced the philosophical William.

"That is the dish I prepare best," boasted Caroline bravely.

"And my favorite," added Alexander, who was helping them to settle in their dismal home. They hoped that he would find employment in London and remain as a member of the household. However, when October arrived, he returned to his position of violoncellist in the Bath orchestra. Nothing they could say would induce him to change his plans.

William returned with him to Bath to tear out and remove the casting equipment from No. 19 New King Street. While there, he cast some small reflectors and one for the twenty-foot Newtonian, which proved useful when a fine reflector was cracked by the January frost.

"Bad beginning, good ending," quoted the invincible Caroline. "It shall be, it must be so now that William has his heart's desire."

The Lady's Comet

9

SETTLED AT DATCHET, the court astronomer promptly began his third review of the heavens, striving to make up for the summer he had lost to lionizing and procrastination. Philosophically, he could not consider the time wholly lost. It had been the price he was obliged to pay for his freedom from musical bondage. It was up to him to make it worthwhile.

While impatiently waiting for the King's decision, he had resolved to make his earlier discoveries, now considered great, to appear as mere trifles. Neither the cold of winter, the heat of summer, the visits of the curious, or the royal summons to Windsor Castle must be allowed to interfere with his resolution.

Curiously, his ambition did not extend to the discovery

of another planet. Neither he nor the astronomers of the theoretical school then suspected the existence of the eighth member of the solar system that was causing irregularities in the motion of his Georgian planet and would inevitably lead to the discovery of the planet Neptune. His intention was to probe deeper and deeper into the structure of the universe with his telescopes, such as no observatory yet had, leaving as he phrased it "no spot in the heavens un-visited."

Caroline, freed from copying music scores and the other petty worries of her musical career, abandoned suddenly and reluctantly, soon found herself struggling valiantly with the problems of country living. It would be a long, long while before she would cease to hanker for the luxury of Bath and the pleasant company of her brother Alexander. Meanwhile, she had resumed her faithful schedule of noting William's observations by night and transcribing his reports for the Royal Society by day.

At this point her brother decided that the time had come for her to begin the pursuit of astronomy in earnest. He built her a small telescope for sweeping, setting it up on a damp grass plot at Datchet. Concerned with how they were to survive on William's new salary, which was hardly half of what he had received at Bath, Caroline was in no mood for "minding the heavens."

Never had a fledgling sweeper a sorrier beginning. Seated uncomfortably on the dew-wet grass, she applied her unaccustomed eyes to the telescope, turning it reluctantly on the unfamiliar heavens. When she sighted what she assumed to be a star cluster or nebula, she called out to her brother for help in identifying its location. If he had been summoned to Windsor Castle by the King, as often happened, she would have to put aside her sweeper and thumb impatiently through her reference book to see what she could make of it alone. More often than not, she failed to find the same spot in the sky when she returned her eyes to the telescope.

It was the utmost in frustration and boredom. Her total of nebulae and star clusters for the whole year was fourteen. She rejoiced when her brother required her at the familiar routine of recording his observations. Through the coldest winter that England had known for many years, she sat at the desk beside the telescope, noting William's findings while the ink froze in the bottle.

In her desperate state of mind, she found a curious release in the messy task of grinding and polishing reflectors. This she could do, seeing and knowing what she was doing. It became the joy of her "leisure hours" that had increased since Bath and the musical chores were left behind. Proudly the tiny female mechanic undertook the polishing and finishing of a very beautiful one for their dear Dr. Watson of Bath. She missed him too, rejoicing when he came to visit them at lonely Datchet.

William employed some of his newly found leisure by building himself a second twenty-foot Newtonian, by far the best and most perfect instrument he ever constructed. It would be known in afteryears in the Herschel family as "the large twenty-foot."

King George ordered four ten-foot Newtonian telescopes as royal gifts, thus putting the Herschel factory into operation. Helpers had to be found to replace the skillful Alexander, who had surprised his family by marrying soon after his return to Bath. Never again would the manufacturers know the days of careless rapture and chaos as at No. 7 New King Street.

"Perhaps it is the price we pay for success," decided Caroline, striving to be philosophical while her brother experimented with substitutes for Alexander—from cheap, untrained laborers to the too-costly watchmaker.

When William began to suffer from the ague at damp, dismal Datchet, he consulted Sir William Watson, physician and scientist of London, who prescribed red bark, wine negus, mutton broth, and similar remedies of the day. When these proved ineffective, he suggested a "healthier spot."

Caroline, who could have forewarned the two eminent scientists from the moment she set eyes on the water-logged old hunting lodge, smothered her I-told-you-so. She patiently packed and repacked her household goods twice before they were comfortably settled at Slough, on April 3, 1786, in the ivy-covered red brick house that was destined to become world famous. By that time they had become so adept at moving that the telescopes used through the previous night were set up in readiness for observation by nightfall.

The house at Slough, which would be known as Herschel

House and Observatory House, was well located on a junction of the London-Bath Road. It sat on an acre of ground bordered with ancient elms. There was a terrace walk affording a lovely view of the imposing walls and towers of Windsor Castle. Altogether it was a charming place. The stable would be converted into workrooms, library, and living quarters known as Observatory Cottage.

Turning his twenty-foot Newtonian on the heavens for his fourth review, the court astronomer was reminded of his dream of a larger telescope with a power then unknown to science. He drew plans for a huge forty-foot Newtonian such as he well knew he could not finance alone. Hopefully he confided his dream to Sir Joseph Banks, the president of the Royal Society, whom he had met on his London visit. Through Sir Joseph's intercession, the King was persuaded to appropriate a sum for the construction and upkeep of the "Great Telescope."

"His Majesty was graciously pleased to approve of it, and with his usual liberality to support it with his Royal bounty," wrote the delighted astronomer.

"We celebrate a milestone, you and I, William," exulted Caroline, whose previously poor opinion of the Royal bounty was modified by her own share in it.

She had been appointed assistant to the court astronomer and granted an annual pension for life from parliament. She could well be grateful for this recognition of her labors in astronomy. She was perhaps the first woman so honored in any field of science. She welcomed the modest pension as the first money she had ever earned, having hitherto been dependent on her brother. She was both proud and humble.

"Now I can crow over Alexander," she continued jubilantly. "He thought I gave up my career when I gave up singing. Perhaps I am finding a new one even as William."

She was approximately the same age as her brother had been when he had launched his astronomical career with the initial entry in his astronomical journal. She had proved her worth by ten years of apprenticeship, as Sir Joseph Banks and the King undoubtedly realized. She knew the tools, the technique, the vocabulary, and the aims of the watchers of the sky. Was she, then, worthy to become one of them?

She had, it is true, made no discoveries of consequence beyond the few nebulae and star clusters which her brother had included in his catalogue with proper credits. However, she could not be considered a stranger to the heavens after recording his explorations into limitless space and the secrets he had wrested from sun, moon, stars, planets, asteroids, nebulae, clusters. Could she make this her vocation?

All that was needed to start her in that direction was the opportunity, and perhaps a slight push. These were promptly supplied by her brother and the King. One of the ten-foot telescopes King George had ordered from the Herschel factory was intended as a gift for the University of Göttingen, founded by his grandfather, who likewise had been king of England and Elector of Hanover. The young university was located about forty miles from the town of Hanover and would doubtless have been William Herschel's alma mater had he been so fortunate as to have one. Its infant observatory was making a name for itself among the older observatories of the region.

Happily the King designated the court astronomer to deliver the gift in person. This could have been a high moment for the self-taught astronomer, recently honored by the University of Edinburgh with the honorary degree of LL.D. He was Dr. Herschel at the age of forty-eight. Alexander went with his brother to Göttingen and to Hanover where they visited their mother and the other members of the family. Alexander left his wife at Slough with Caroline. For the sisters-in-law, this was a getting-to-know-you visit since they had not met in Bath.

William assigned to his assistant the task of supervising the workmen at Slough. Already the ancient elms had been felled to make way for the "Great Telescope." The stone foundations had been laid and the wooden supporting stand erected. A smith was preparing the forge for the construction of the giant tube. The reflector was being ground and polished by a crew of workmen.

As a gesture of appreciation and farewell, William had constructed "an excellent small Newtonian Sweeper" for his sister. Little did he then suspect that it would become almost as famous as his own "Great Telescope" that would be the eighth wonder of the world for a span of fifty years. He put it in position on the flat roof of the converted stables known as Observatory Cottage.

"Lina," he said, presenting it, "may it be another milestone in your career."

"William, I had not hoped to have such a fine sweeper of my very own," she said, recalling the time when he could not afford the smallest of instruments and so had involved the Bath household in the chaos of invention and manufacture. "I thank you, Dr. Herschel."

"I wish you good luck and good sweeping, Lina. Let me have an account of your progress."

"*Auf wiedersehen,* William. Give my love to Mamma and Dietrich."

"Not to Jacob?"

"Jacob will hardly expect my love." She could not forget the unhappiness he had caused her as a child.

"Take good care of Mrs. H.," charged Alexander.

"I shall do my best. I'll be thinking of you, Alexander, when I use the Monkey Clock you made for me. *Auf wiedersehen!*"

With the slowed tempo at Slough during her brother's absence, Caroline found time for little chores about the workrooms, such as polishing the brass instrument parts and hanging curtains to keep the dust from the shelves of supplies. She wound the two clocks which she would use for her solitary sweeping—the sidereal clock and the so-called "Monkey Clock," the loud-ticking metronomic device that Alexander had invented for her.

When the iron plates to be used in constructing the giant tube were delivered, half of them bad, she hired a helper for the smith.

The old gardener proved a vexation, coming daily

though William had said he would be needed only three days a week. When she refused to pay him for the unauthorized time, he reported in the village that she was "stingy."

She took her sister-in-law shopping in the village and calling on the neighbors, trying to choose a time that would be free from official guests. Once they returned to learn that three foreign gentlemen had called and departed without leaving their names. That was humiliating; William would not be pleased when he heard about it, or the King either. Already princes, noblemen, and those she termed "philosophical gentlemen" were making a path to the door of Observatory House. Astronomers, too, were coming, from Paris, Milan, Palermo, Cracow.

Caroline's professional assignment for this interlude was the cataloging of all the nebulae her brother had discovered. This was, of course, her daytime task; her nights were dedicated to sweeping. When twilight returned and the stars reappeared, one by one, above the dreaming valley of the Thames, she climbed to her small sweeper on the flat roof of the converted stables. This was quite a different matter from her frustrated sweeping at Datchet. The surroundings were more congenial. Furthermore, there was the challenge of her appointment as assistant to the court astronomer. For William's sake as well as her own, she must sweep, she must discover.

The evening of August 1, 1786, arrived. By half-past nine the twilight had deepened enough for sweeping. The observer, frankly owning herself "a bad or no observer at all, having in three years not looked as many times in the telescope," climbed to her small sweeper on the roof of Observatory Cottage. She began her sweeping "in the neighborhood of the sun for comets." By ten o'clock she saw "an object resembling in color and brightness 27 Nebula of Messier with the difference of being rotund." To her it seemed "like a star out of focus though the rest were perfectly distinct." Could it be a comet? she asked herself excitedly.

A haziness spread over the Thames valley, ending her sweeping and speculations. In her diary she noted tersely, "This evening I saw an object which I believe will prove tomorrow night to be a comet." She recorded its position in the heavens, making drawings of the familiar stars in the field of view. The mysterious "object" lay in an obtuse triangle between two stars of *Ursae Majoris,* the constellation of the Great Bear, and three stars of *Coma Berenices,* the constellation of Berenice's Hair.

On August 2 it rained all day. When the skies cleared an hour after midnight, Caroline was at her post, eager to resolve the mystery of the "object." Confidently she noted in her diary, "The object of last night *is a Comet.*" With professional pride, she announced her discovery to Dr. Blagden, the secretary of the Royal Society, enclosing her drawings of its position in the heavens. Two cloudy nights followed, halting further sweeping. She wrote the news to William and to Dietrich, who had his own telescope in Hanover.

On August 5 her entry read, "The night was tolerably

fair and I saw the Comet." The next night Sir Joseph Banks and Dr. Blagden called at Slough, bringing Lord Palmerston with them to see the comet through her telescope and to congratulate the first woman to have discovered a comet.

"Bravo, Lina!" William and Alexander, crossing her letter enroute, returned in mid-August to share the excitement. The so-called "Lady's Comet" and the lady discoverer were sensations, sharing headlines, stares, conversations. "Very little, very gentle, very modest, very ingenious," was the impression of Fanny Burney, the celebrated diarist and novelist, of the comet-finder. She had perhaps expected something "very" different of the lady with the "eccentric vocation."

"You have immortalized your name," wrote an English astronomer by way of congratulation. A French astronomer named his daughter Caroline in her honor. Others referred to her as "the priestess of the heavens."

Though Caroline Herschel's priority of discovery was undisputed, the comet received no honorary christening, being known only as "the Lady's Comet." There was perhaps no other lady discoverer in the history of astronomy, that most ancient science.

More Comets, More Fame

10

VISITORS TO SLOUGH in the late summer of 1786 en-
countered a chaos of construction on the lawn of Observatory House. William Herschel was rushing the erection of
his "Great Telescope," which had been delayed by his
journey to Göttingen. Wearing workman's clothes, he super-
vised an army of laborers, "common workmen," through
each step of the construction. Caroline shuddered as she
watched him stretched for hours at a time on a high beam
in the sun. It was a wonder he did not suffer a heatstroke
or fall to his death. He had met with several serious acci-
dents since he had begun the study of astronomy.

His sister likewise was a veteran of casualties. One night,
while trudging through a foot of snow, she had fallen on
an iron hook "such as butchers use for hanging their joints

on." It entered her right leg above the knee. When she failed to appear at her post, William and his assistant began shouting for her to hurry. Unable to free herself, she called faintly, "I'm hooked."

They could not release her from the hook without leaving "two ounces of flesh behind." She applied her home remedies to have the wound grow worse. The doctor she called told her that a soldier with such a wound would spend six weeks in a hospital. Soldier Caroline had limped faithfully to her post every night, except when clouds made observation impossible.

The "Great Telescope" was a masterpiece of inventive skill, introducing techniques not then generally known. It had been designed in infinite detail down to the last "screw bolt." The huge supporting stand was of timbers, themselves supported by a method later to be known as diagonal bracing. The titan tube was of iron, one-twentieth of an inch thick, proofed against rust and erosion by a process later used on corrugated iron roofing.

Lying on the lawn at Slough, awaiting erection, the tube was inspected by countless curious visitors of all degrees, who found a special delight in walking through its great length. The observant Miss Fanny Burney noted that she could have paraded through it with ease in her largest feathered hat and widest hoops.

One day Caroline looked out to see the King, the Queen, the Duke of York, the Princess Royal, and the Princess Augusta, with an attending company of lords and ladies, arriving from Windsor Castle. "Ah, the King is inspecting the tube," she cried. "Will he also walk through it?"

She saw him boldly entering and turning to extend a royal hand to his companion, the Archbishop of Canterbury. "Come, my Lord Bishop," said King George to the hesitating prelate, "I will show you the way to heaven."

Truly it was the way to undiscovered heavens. After annoying delays, the promenades through the tube were terminated by a gala inaugural. The Herschel family and their guests left the dinner table to gather on the lawn where they joined in singing "God Save the King," led by George Griesbach with his oboe and impromptu musicians with any instruments they could lay hands on. The light-hearted, light-footed Caroline led the rejoicing cavalcade through the tube.

The delays had been caused by difficulties with the huge four-foot reflector. For this, William had allowed a London caster to talk him into the use of an alloy whose formula the caster had refused to reveal. When polished and placed in position, it proved unsatisfactory, for it "was too thin to give a good figure." Impatient for his first look, the court astronomer turned the huge instrument on the Georgian planet for a test.

The sight that met his eyes seemed wholly unrewarding. He saw "some very faint stars" near the planet, which was likewise very faint even with the powerful instrument. Over the years he had developed a unique philosophy on the art of seeing. He had come to believe that "you must

102

not expect to see on sight." His years of experience had convinced him that "seeing is in some respects an art which must be learnt." Instead of turning from the "Great Telescope" in defeat that night of January 11, 1787, he applied his theory.

Night after night he turned the instrument on the barely visible specks that a novice might have dismissed as so many fireflies. Keeping one of the specks in view for a period of nine hours, he was able to see it "faithfully attending its primary planet." He had discovered a satellite of Uranus, his planet.

Further observation revealed what he suspected to be a second satellite. Repeating his patient procedure, he was rewarded by the sight of "the Georgian Planet attended by two satellites." For five hours he watched the awe-inspiring spectacle of the fairy moons which of course would be named Oberon and Titania. Five hours of discoverer's delight! It was such ecstasy as this that the poet Keats would envision in his sonnet of the coming century.

"The prose of heaven surpasses the brightest poetry of earth" was the way Herschel put it. He suspected the existence of other moons of the Georgian planet, but even with his powerful instrument and sensitivity of vision, he was unable to see them. The fairy satellites were mere specks, as he wrote, "very nearly the dimmest objects that can be seen in the heavens." It would be sixty years before the discovery of the infinitesimal companion moons of Oberon and Titania, Ariel and Umbriel.

Assistant Caroline was provided with a luxury she had had not known previously, a shelter at the base of the telescope. There she recorded her brother's dictation coming through a "speaking-pipe" from one-hundred-fifteen feet above her. In this manner she shared in the discovery of the fairy moons. Later she noted in her journal, "My brother showed me the *G. Sidus* in the twenty-foot telescope, and I saw both the satellites very plainly."

These epochal results spurred the perfecting of the reflector. A second one was cast of the speculum metal formula used at Bath. It cracked in cooling. It was recast, polished, tried, found wanting, perfected for a year and a half before it was brought to "such a figure and polish" as was desired by the inventor. Satisfied that his telescope was finished, Herschel turned it on Saturn, the planet that had been its chief inspiration.

Once he had seen it as "a ball of yarn with the rings as knitting needles projecting through it on both sides." Now, on September 17, 1789, he saw it clearly "with six satellites in such a situation and so bright as rendered it impossible to mistake them." Only five satellites of Saturn were previously known. He had made another epochal discovery—the sixth satellite of Saturn which would be christened "Enceladus."

Watching for three weeks, he located a seventh satellite, so small and so close to the planet that it had eluded detection. From continuing observations he was led to suspect the presence of an eighth moon of Saturn among the "beads

104

of light." With his superbly trained vision, he was never able to see it. The seventh satellite was named "Mimas." The atmospheric rings whose mystery had eluded him for many years continued to do so even with the "Great Telescope."

Meanwhile, the great Dr. Herschel, at the age of fifty, had surprised his friends and particularly his sister by marrying the widow of a neighbor whose company and excellent library he had frequently enjoyed. His bride was a gracious, charming, wealthy woman, fitted in every way to become the hostess of Herschel House. It was said that King George was pleased, indeed had fostered the romance.

They were married at Upton Church in the village of that name between Slough and Eton. William's good friend, Sir Joseph Banks, had acted as his best man. Alexander and Caroline attended the ceremony and signed the register, then Caroline hurried home to supervise the serving of the wedding breakfast.

The marriage had been a great shock to Caroline. She had known that her handsome brother had been considered a catch by the ladies of Bath. There he had kept himself aloof, preferring his own small parties to the gaieties of the Pump-Room and Assembly. Since he had successfully eluded their wiles, she had erred in assuming that he would remain a bachelor for life.

She confided her sorrow to her diary, discreetly destroying it in after years lest it should be read by those who might be hurt by it. To turn the management of Herschel

House to another could have been a relief to the busy sister-assistant; evidently it was not. She moved out, to the living quarters in Observatory Cottage; the bride and groom honeymooned in Observatory House.

Caroline Herschel's position as assistant to her brother continued without interruption. Whenever opportunity offered, which was seldom, she swept for comets. Curiosity spurred her to sweep for a comet announced as the discovery of Messier, her French contemporary. She failed to find it but soon made her own second discovery, recorded as "preceding *Beta* of *Lyra*," the constellation of the Harp. Her brother, seeing it with his ten-foot Newtonian, proudly announced her discovery to Sir Joseph Banks of the Royal Society.

With the passing of another year, Caroline doubled her score of comets. Her fourth discovery, located as "following *Alpha* of *Andromedae* in a place where there is no nebula," was a delight and a near-frustration. Her brother was vacationing in Yorkshire. Her new five-foot Newtonian sweeper was not half finished. She persevered with her observations alone and proudly announced her discovery.

Again congratulations arrived from English and foreign astronomers. Lalande of the Paris Observatory addressed his letter to *Astronome Célèbre*, Slough." In thanking him, Caroline Herschel inquired about her god-daughter Caroline.

At Slough, the discovery of the year 1792 was termed by his aunt, in humorous vein, "the Herschel planetoid." John Frederick William Herschel, the only child of Caroline's beloved brother, was an adorable and precocious boy

106

whom she took to her heart, dubbing him "Sir John" some thirty years in advance of his knighting by King William IV. In this, she was perhaps voicing her impatience at King George's long delayed knighting of her brother.

The adoring aunt proudly followed the career of her nephew from his petticoat days spent in the shadow of the famous telescope to his culminating observations at the Cape of Good Hope nearly a half-century later. Their mutually tender relationship was a source of great comfort to the lonely old lady after the death of her brother and her retirement to Hanover.

She shared his childish games in chemistry, contributing bottle caps, teacups and other miniature equipment. To the amusement of his parents, she attempted to teach him astronomy at an early age. Following his academic career at St. John's College, Cambridge, where he entered at seventeen and graduated at twenty-one, she rejoiced when "he took all the firsts in sight."

Aunt Caroline added to her score of comets a fifth, sixth, seventh, and eighth. Her eighth and last was her pet, discovered on August 14, 1797. All the others had been telescopic. This one she first saw with the naked eye, as she had seen Edmund Halley's great comet above Hanover long ago. The discovery occurred when she "began in her usual manner looking over the heavens as soon as it became dark enough for sweeping." Excitedly she ran down from her observatory to call Alexander to help with the Monkey Clock.

In her Book of Sweepings, she listed it possessively as

107

"C. H.'s Comet." Her devoted nephew, who was five years old at the time of the discovery, referred to it as "yours." Of her eight discoveries, five were indisputably hers, yet none was named for her. Happily, she cared little for such division of the spoils, deeming it like the childhood game of "Kicks," played with apples in Hanover.

Caroline Herschel's comet-searching was ended by circumstances seemingly beyond her control. She was crowded from Observatory Cottage by the accumulation of the years. She moved into lodgings but found the loss of time getting to and from work a great vexation, as was the transportation. Transcribing reports and papers in her isolated rooms, she was irked by not having access to books and references at the moment she needed them. She met with many unpleasant experiences which kept her moving from lodging to lodging. Even in Mrs. Herschel's beautiful Upton House, she found herself crowded from her rooms by the accumulation of optical parts for the telescope being manufactured for the King of Spain, a masterpiece almost equal to the "Great Telescope."

Happier interludes occurred when her brother and his wife left for their annual vacations. Then Caroline was invited to return to Observatory House in her former capacity as hostess to the visiting great and near-great. When Alexander's wife died, he joined Caroline there, helping with the grinding and polishing as in the good old days at Bath. Then the brother and sister led more relaxed lives, though idleness was not a Herschel trait.

William would leave the chaise for her to use in calling on the neighbors. Once, at Windsor Castle, she had been surprised to have a lady-in-waiting to Queen Charlotte recognize her as a fellow-pupil at Madame Kuster's dressmaking school in Hanover. She was now Mrs. Beckedorff. Caroline remembered her as one of the younger pupils who had shared those briefly happy schooldays. After that they visited with each other, dining and teaing at Windsor Castle and at Buckingham House when the Court had returned to London for the winter. The Royal Princesses were thrilled to welcome the famous little lady of the comets. Miss Fanny Burney, who had become a lady-in-waiting to Queen Charlotte, was equally thrilled to meet her.

Caroline Herschel had no bonafide vacations during all those long years. Once her brother had sent her to make some corrections in the Index to Flamsteed's Observations of the Fixed Stars, at the Greenwich Observatory. Dr. Maskelyne, the Astronomer Royal whom William once called "a devil of a fellow," received her royally. With Mrs. Maskelyne and their daughter, he entertained her so continuously that she could hardly find time to make her corrections. Indeed, she had little time for sleeping.

As William's health broke with overwork and age, he often went to the nearby resorts for relief. When he and Mrs. Herschel rented a house in Bath for the season, Caroline went in advance, making an inventory of the furnishings and putting them in order for the occupants. Then she visited Alexander in his lonely home, putting things in

109

order there before returning to Slough to act as hostess for Observatory House.

William Herschel never attempted to surpass his "Great Telescope" as to size; in fact, he found the large one cumbersome to use, always preferring his twenty-footer. He constantly improved the mirrors for the smaller instruments, finding ways to adjust them for better light and vision. As his strength failed, he relaxed the tiring night-long observations, concentrating on the assembling of his forty years of accumulated studies.

Caroline worried about his poor health and low spirits, fretting when visitors to the observatory kept him for long hours without proper rest and food. She worried also about her own failing strength, fearing that she might be exhausted before he was. That must not happen. She carried on valiantly, rejoicing over his belated honors.

At long last the Prince Regent created William Herschel a Knight of the Royal Hanoverian Guelphic Order, an honor too long delayed by his father, King George III, who had been incapacitated by insanity. The veteran astronomer became Sir William Herschel at the age of seventy-eight. He helped to organize the Royal Astronomical Society of London, becoming its first president, with his son John its first secretary.

In 1821 Sir William looked for the last time at the stars through one of his telescopes. A year later, at the age of eighty-four, he died and was buried in Upton Church where he had been married. Alexander had suffered an accident, ending his long and honored career as musician at Bath and Bristol. William had provided for him, sending him home to Hanover where he died. Caroline Herschel was alone with her memories of fifty years of companionship to her best of brothers.

Awards, Medals, Honors

11

WITHOUT HER BROTHER and her work, once happy England would be only a desolation to Caroline. She knew she could not face the loneliness and constant reminder of her loss. Impulsively she decided to return to Hanover, her birthplace, which she had left as a young woman of twenty-two and had never revisited.

At seventy-two, she was turning from the conquest of space to the conquest of grief and loneliness—the equivalent of a vocation not less valiant than her earlier ones. She was a frail, elderly woman, stunned by her sorrow. Many of her former companions were gone. The men of science—Sir Joseph Banks, Sir William Watson, and others who had been her brother's associates and hers—had died, as had King George and Queen Charlotte. After the passing of the

Queen, Mrs. Beckedorff, Caroline's schooldays friend, had returned to Hanover with her daughter.

Dietrich Herschel, the baby of the family, now an aging man of sixty-seven, lived in Hanover with his family. Though he had never been as close to her as William and Alexander and often had been a problem to them all, it seemed natural and comforting to turn to him now. He not only welcomed her into his home but came to meet her for the crossing of the stormy North Sea. It was a touching gesture, one that William might have made, or Papa or Alexander.

Lady Herschel, nephew John, and dear friends joined them in London for a final farewell, which Caroline termed "an everlasting leave." With Dietrich, her trunks, the portrait of her beloved brother, and her famous sweepers, Caroline went aboard the steam packet at the Thames docks near the Tower of London. The crossing was no less rough under steam than sail. Lacking the stamina of youth, she suffered much distress, arriving exhausted on the coast of Holland.

In Hanover, Dietrich's wife had prepared an attractive apartment for her in their home so that she might live and feel independent. It might have seemed the perfect setting for the retired astronomer whose seven-foot Newtonian sweeper kept her company in a corner of the room.

Hanover, however, was a bitter disappointment to her. "Abominable city," she called it, finding nothing as she had anticipated. The people were not the same as they had been fifty years ago. Their ways were not the ways she recalled and she did not approve of them. The world seemed a sorry place. Dietrich, her closest relative, who should have been a comfort to her, proved to be an obstinate, crochety old man. He was poor company for the sister who yearned for the scientific and learned companions she had known at Slough. When she recalled an incident of their childhood one way, he perversely recalled it another.

His daughter Anna, the Widow Knipping, was a devoted niece, compensating for her father's short temper and exasperating ways. Mrs. Beckedorff and her daughter were equally comforting to the self-exiled old lady. Nothing, however, cheered her lonely life so much as the letters of her adored nephew, the handsome young bachelor who had inherited his father's telescopes, apparatus, and wealth, as well as his talents. When he gave up the profession of law to become an astronomer, she was thrilled, stirred from her stupor.

His research on binary, or double, stars reminded her of his father's studies in that field, begun at Bath and continued through his long and brilliant career. This had been the basis of many voluminous reports on "The Interior Construction of the Universe," all of which she had patiently transcribed for preservation by the Royal Society.

With enthusiasm, she wrote her nephew of her memories of his father's observations on double stars. Meanwhile, she was grieving that in her isolation there was no one to appreciate or share her joy. How William would have rejoiced to see his son carrying on his great work! Excitedly she searched among her books for the three-volume set of Locke's *Essay Concerning Human Understanding*. William had bought it on his first trip to England at the age of eighteen. This precious memento, containing "the date and his name in his beautiful handwriting," she sent to nephew John.

In her heart, she knew that the time had come for her to shake off her shameful inaction. William could never stand to be idle, nor could she in their years together. Spurred by her memories, she turned from her idleness and grief. She resolved to work, work, work. It was what she knew and longed for; it would be her salvation.

Wisely she had brought from Slough a mass of manuscripts and books of sweepings to be catalogued. She undertook the cataloguing of twenty-five hundred nebulae as a labor of love for the use of her nephew in his new vocation. The slow, tedious task occupied her for five years, providing the wings for lifting her from her provincial surroundings to the regions she had known and loved, from the atmosphere of crabbed age to happy youthful memories.

John was pleased with her great work. The Royal Astronomical Society of London awarded her a Gold Medal for her outstanding contribution to science. As the president of the Society, John refused to make the presentation on the plea of kinship. He insisted that he had not proposed the medal or had anything to do with it; however, he could not have prevented it if he chose. When Caroline misunderstood his words to convey a slight of some sort, he wrote back assuring her that it was a great honor which she deserved. It was indeed rare for a woman's work in science to be so recognized.

Sir John Herschel, recently knighted by King William IV, completed his revision of his father's sweepings, adding to them his own discoveries. He then looked about in search of more worlds to conquer. His choice was the southern hemisphere. When told of his proposed expedition to the Cape of Good Hope, Aunt Caroline's blue eyes blazed with enthusiasm. It was a project after her own heart. Had she been thirty years younger, she would have joined him and Lady Herschel in spite of the two months' sea voyage involved. Alas, she was eighty-three, no better than a prisoner in abominable Hanover!

Sir John's lengthy letters from the Cape she considered "like a drop of oil supplying my expiring lamp." For his observations, he had chosen a site at Feldhausen, "a perfect paradise," between Table Bay and Table Mountain. The scenery, woods, and flowers defied description; the constellations were of astonishing brilliancy.

Fortunately he had his twenty-foot Newtonian set up in time for the periodical reappearance of Halley's Comet; he was able to make some studies of it. He tried to catch a glimpse of Encke's Comet, "yours," he called it, but he had failed even with the sacrifice of a beautiful strip of woodland. These were names to bring back memories of Papa and her first view of Halley's Comet over the Parade

Ground in Hanover long ago, as well as her later comet-spangled career.

In the clear, dry atmosphere of the Cape, Sir John turned his telescope on Uranus, the Georgian planet, his father's great discovery. He saw the two fairy moons, Oberon and Titania, sighted only rarely since their discovery at Slough fifty years before. These, too, were magic names for Aunt Caroline, who was something of a sprite herself. They took her back to days of youth and glory. She was wild with excitement in her lonely room in Hanover.

Sir John's observations of the planet Saturn could hardly have been less thrilling for her. The studies which her brother had made and she had recorded were almost beyond the counting, all faithfully transcribed for the Royal Society. Sir John now saw for his first time the sixth satellite of Saturn, which his father had discovered at Slough with his "Great Telescope." He called it "Mr. Sixth." Try as he would, he could not see the infinitesimal "Mr. Seventh," which had so nearly eluded his father's sharper eyes.

These were perhaps sentimental journeys designed especially for the delight of Aunt Caroline. Sir John Herschel's great expedition was dedicated to the study of the double stars and nebulae of the southern hemisphere. For four years he pursued his observations in the clear, dry atmosphere of the Cape, adding more than seventeen hundred findings. These he would combine with the discoveries of his father and others in the northern hemisphere—including Aunt Caroline's findings at damp, dismal Datchet.

117

While Sir John was pursuing his observations thousands of miles away, Aunt Caroline was busily compiling her final astronomical catalogues, her swan song to the stars. She completed "A Catalogue of Eight Hundred and Sixty Stars Observed by Flamsteed But not included in the British Catalogue." Then she followed it with "A General Index of Reference to Every Observation of Every Star in the above mentioned British Catalogue."

"An immense labor . . . an extraordinary monument," pronounced the Royal Society of London, awarding her an honorary membership. She was eighty-five. The townfolk of Hanover called it her "promotion." The familiar, tiny figure, going nimbly to theater and concert, receiving the salutes of all, must have been secretly pleased to be "stared at for a learned lady."

The year 1838 was the centennial of the birth of William Herschel. In that year, the two living Herschel astronomers made the headlines—the forty-six-year-old nephew and the eighty-eight-year-old aunt. Sir John, concluding what astronomers referred to as "the greatest scientific expedition in the history of astronomy," returned to London to be honored and feted by the learned societies, and created a baron by the young Queen Victoria at her coronation. Before this excitement had subsided, Aunt Caroline was elected to honorary membership in the Royal Irish Academy, Dublin. Her surprise and pleasure were tempered by the fact that she had not discovered a comet for many years, almost a lifetime.

Sir John brought his six-year-old-son to Hanover to surprise his Great-aunt Caroline. Thinking to trick her, he sent the child into her room with a friend, waiting outside the door to see how his scheme came off.

"What little boy is that?" she asked when the bright-eyed youngster was led before her.

"The son of a friend of mine," answered the escort. The boy said nothing, as he had been instructed. She was to guess who he was.

She tried another approach. "Where do you come from, little fellow?"

"From the Cape of Good Hope." He had perhaps spoken out of turn, not having been properly warned.

Now she was beginning to catch on, getting warmer. "Who is he? What's his name? Is it Herschel?"

She had guessed. "Herschel, William James Herschel." He was the only grandson, the namesake of her beloved brother.

Sir John, the rascal, came into the room and sat down beside her. She began talking to him as if five minutes instead of five years had passed since their last meeting. Her concern lest some harm befall "Little Willie" almost effaced the joy of the visit. Hoping to lessen the pang of parting for her, Sir John left early in the morning before she was awake. Her disappointment at finding them gone was overwhelming. Soon she was writing, begging Sir John and Lady Herschel not to come again; she could no longer bear the pain of parting from anyone so precious. She would be satisfied with their letters and those of "Little Willie" and "Little Caroline," her namesake whom she had not seen.

From Kent, where the Herschel family had located after their return from the Cape, Sir John had gone for a visit to the shrine at Slough, which he had inherited. He found the wooden scaffolding of the "Great Telescope" decayed beyond repair. There was nothing he could do but take it down. He made a ceremony of the event, just as one had been made for its erection fifty years before. He composed a ballad as requiem to be sung by the assembled Herschel family at midnight, New Year's, 1839–1840.

The giant tube was laid horizontally on low stone piers, with the machinery and parts sealed within. For years thereafter, it was to be seen on the lawn at Slough with a bust of Sir William Herschel on a pedestal nearby. "It looks very well in its new location," wrote Sir John to Aunt Caroline. In afteryears, a church was built on the site once occupied by the famous telescope.

The ceremony of tearing down the "Great Telescope" wakened poignant memories in Caroline Herschel, who so nimbly had led the cavalcade through the giant tube on Inaugural Day so long ago. Now, alas, she must put on nimbleness as an armor when she went out on the streets to be stared at. In the privacy of her room, her feet sometimes faltered. Her eyesight was also failing, causing her to lament, "The few, few stars I can get out of my window only cause me vexation." In these days, she was perfecting her technique for the conquest of loneliness and age, confessing, "My sole employment is keeping myself in good humor."

After the death of her brother Dietrich, she had moved to other rooms where she seemed happier. She was learning to adjust to the life of the town, subscribing to plays two evenings a week and having her "at home" in winter as the other ladies of Hanover did. This she explained as a local version of a learned society or bluestocking club where the talk was of Sir Walter Scott, Lord Byron, and other literary lions.

Her "painful solitude" was cheered by the faithful Mrs. Knipping, Mrs. Beckedorff and her daughter. Learned men on visits to the town seldom failed to pay their respects to the famous little lady. She thrilled to hear Paganini, the celebrated Italian violinist, when "he filled the play-house twice at double price." Leaving her box after the concert, she found him waiting at the door with a group of gentlemen. He had asked to be introduced to her. They talked through an interpreter.

By her ventures into night life, she was seeking valiantly to forget what she called her "severed situation." One of the royal princesses she had known in England gave her a "very handsome fur mantle" for evening wear. This was a timely prop for her morale. She could usually feel braver when upheld by such finery. Once when the King came into her box to inquire about her health, she had wept and was ashamed.

At the recital of Ole Bull, the Norwegian violinist, she

had been disappointed. Expecting a virtuoso in the manner of her brothers Jacob and Dietrich, she had found his playing more of a "conjuration." This implied compliment to Jacob was the extent of her praise for that brother who had been the villain of her childhood.

Comets Were Her Line

12

By the time Caroline Herschel reached her ninetieth milestone, the celebration of her birthday, March 16, had become a tradition in Hanover. From noon to four o'clock she kept open house, receiving the local royalty and her friends who came with the lovely March flowers that were her birthright —crocus, hyacinth, violet. Some of them brought the more exotic moss roses and mignonette. The Crown Prince and Princess came, arm in arm, bringing an immense bouquet of roses from the royal greenhouses. The King of Prussia sent splendid gifts from Berlin.

These happy birthdays were exhilarating to the point of exhaustion for the frail, elderly lady. Once she confessed to talking herself into a fever that prevented her from sleeping for two nights thereafter. It was then, in the silence, that there began to unroll in her active mind the amazing drama of the little maid of Hanover who had been Caroline Lucretia Herschel.

Excitedly she began to set it all down, writing her *History of the Herschels,* to be published later as her memoirs. She sent it in installments to the Herschel family at Collingwood, Kent. Lady Herschel read these to Little Willie, Little Caroline and the other young Herschels. All were enchanted, demanding more.

Even Sir John had known very little of that poor but wonderful family that came to life in her pages. Born when his father was fifty-four, he remembered him only as a middle-aged gentleman—wealthy, successful, a world-famous astronomer, associate of scientists of England and all Europe.

There had been nothing to suggest his humble beginning as an oboist in the Hanoverian Guards' Band at the age of fourteen, or his thirty years as a professional musician. Equally incredible was his switch to astronomy so late in life. He was wholly self-taught, yet able to produce the most startling discoveries with his homemade instruments. So greatly had he improved the telescope that people were inclined to think that he had invented it. No wonder!

Aunt Caroline's life likewise was full of the unsuspected and amazing—her unhappy childhood, her intense longing to be more than a household drudge, her success as a singer in a strange language and country, her sacrifice of it all for the sake of her brother, followed by her astonishing career in astronomy. Sir John Herschel had heard of a young woman astronomer, Maria Mitchell, who visited him later on in America. Aunt Caroline, however, was the pioneer of her sex. A truly incredible character!

It could all be traced back, he was convinced as he read, to the poor, self-taught musician, Isaac Herschel, who had taught his children to be musicians and instilled in them a love of learning, believing that the legacy he gave them was little indeed. What a glorious inheritance they had made of it, each one!

Completing the *History of the Herschels,* the historian laid down her pen to write no more. Miss Beckedorff wrote her letters for her, keeping the family in Kent informed of her failing strength and eyesight. When Sir John's presentation copy of his *Cape Observations* arrived, she was not able to read it; it had to be read to her.

By this time she had disposed of her sweepers. She gave the five-foot Newtonian to the Royal Astronomical Society of London where she trusted it would be preserved, as was the little telescope of Sir Isaac Newton, by the Royal Society.

She would not live to see that final meeting of astronomical greats when Sir John Herschel would be buried near the tomb of Sir Isaac Newton in Westminster Abbey. Perhaps she would have felt that Sir William in his lonely tomb at Upton had been slighted, that he was deserving of more than the simple memorial stone in the floor of the Abbey near those other two. To her, he was the greatest of them all. How much she contributed to that greatness,

125

historians have not failed to note.

When the biographies of her beloved brother began to appear, she watched eagerly for their arrival, cherishing the ones that she deemed worthy, longing to burn the ones she did not, yet never daring because of their handsome bindings. She could only scorn them in secret as she scorned all the superficial references to her comets. Astronomer Olbers of the Bremen Observatory she respected because he, having seen each of her discoveries, knew whereof he had written.

Each birthday found the nonagenarian slightly frailer but no less valiant. On her ninety-sixth anniversary, in 1846, she was honored by the King of Prussia with a Gold Medal for Science.

On her ninety-seventh birthday, dressed in a new cap and gown by Betty, her "jewel of a servant," she received her guests, bright-eyed, tremulous, perhaps a little proud to have outwitted the "Destroying Angel" for another year. The Crown Prince and Princess brought the usual royal roses, a cake, and a resplendent velvet armchair.

Shortly before her next birthday, Caroline Lucretia Herschel "fell asleep in a calm rest and in full possession of her faculties." She was buried in the Hanover churchyard near the grave of her father. On her tombstone was inscribed the epitaph she had prepared, bearing witness to "Her own Discoveries of Comets and her participation in the immortal labors of her Brother, Sir William Herschel."

Friends planted a white rosebush on her grave. Astronomers belatedly honored her in the heavens by naming an asteroid Lucretia. Small honor, she might have thought it, to be associated with a so-called "nuisance of the skies." Comets were her line.